Tech Girl
Diaries

Tech Girl *Diaries*

A Girl's Ongoing Journey in STEM

JOY MAKUMBE

CONTENTS

FOREWORD

I am delighted to write this foreword, not only because Joy Makumbe has been a friend and colleague for more than twenty years, but also because I believe deeply in the practice of gender equality. I also believe that women have the mental capacity to process and execute any technical task just as the next man, if not better because they have had to prove themselves over and over again.

I first met Joy at the University of Zimbabwe where she was studying civil engineering and I was pursuing a degree in information technology. From that time to date, I can strongly say that Joy knows a thing or two about beating the odds in a male-dominated field. Over the years, as a civil engineer and entrepreneur, she has made a name for herself in the world of water and sanitation, which has long been considered a boy's club.

In 2004, she founded Majorlic Construction, an engineering and green tech company that specializes in water and sanitation infrastructure projects. She has been involved in projects based in Zimbabwe, Tanzania, and Uganda. Her accomplishments include senior engineering roles in a World Bank-funded water project in the western Ugandan town of Bushenyi and a European Investment Bank project in the Tanzanian port city of Mwanza, on the shore of Lake Victoria. In founding and running her own firm, Joy joined a small number of female C.E.O's in a sector where males overwhelmingly outnumber women, particularly in leadership positions.

Not even the challenges of motherhood and working in an industry and in cultures where gender discrimination and sexual harassment are common was enough to deter her from succeeding. If anything, Joy says facing the gender gap has made her even more driven, fuelling her desire to pay that success forward.

Recognizing that the glass ceiling is especially difficult to shatter in the engineering sector, she is determined to help other women to overcome hurdles, obstacles, and roadblocks that stand in their way. The key to bridging the gender gap, according to Joy, is supporting the push for more females in technical fields. And although she never had a professional mentor herself, she understands the importance of mentorship, particularly for girls and women. In her own words, she has always said,

"I am passionate about inspiring women and girls. I want them to see that engineering is not gender-based. This means beefing up the current numbers of women joining tech professions and I am determined to use all available channels to achieve this."

This is what gave birth to the Tech Girl Diaries project, a book about Joy's tech journey in a domain predominantly male-dominated. She takes you on a very personal journey, told with intense emotion. A journey from a childhood that helped shape her passion for STEM, to navigating the engineering professional arena. Her pains, struggles, and achievements highlight the prejudice female engineers face in this field.

Told in a fun and captivating way, this book will motivate and inspire every girl that has ever dreamed of becoming anything more than she was told she could be. The book will inspire any young female who seeks to unlock the barriers that cloud many females by exposing stale trends. It is for that parent that sees potential in their little girl but does not know how to support her, and the men in communities who want to support women in originally male-dominated fields but have no idea where to start. The book is for everyone that relates to the professional plight of women in STEM careers.

I have had to work twice as hard as my male colleagues to get to where I am today. I have been sidelined for promotions all because I was a woman and my bosses did not feel I could handle the pressure. I was not even given the opportunity to prove myself.

Being a mother of two girls, I do not wish for them to be prejudiced based on their gender. I hope that this book will become a blueprint for girls, boys, men, women, and educators to learn how they all can play a part in destroying patriarchy that has gripped our societies and generalized what is acceptable and what is not. I foresee this book removing the red tape in peoples' minds that has hindered many women and girls from pursuing the careers and lives of their dreams.

This book is definitely a must read!

Yeukai Makoni
IT Engineer

DEDICATION

To all the people who helped me put this book out there:

My parents, Elisha and Irene, who gave me life,

Gaily and Glenda, for being my sounding
boards and never complaining,

Francisca Mandeya, whose guidance I greatly treasure,

My troop of strong women, who always lift me up.

And Tanatswa, my daughter, a strong woman in the making,
and the reason I get out of bed every morning.

PREFACE

My name is Joy Pedzisayi Makumbe, and I was raised in Harare, the capital of Zimbabwe. The city is in the Mashonaland region, which is the area of the country where most ethnic Shona-speaking people live. Between Mashonaland and Matabeleland, which comprises predominantly Ndebele-speaking people, these two groups make up 94% of the country's total population.[1]

The various families and ethnicities of Zimbabwe are made up of various clans who identify by their totems; typically, either a natural object or an animate being, such as an animal or bird. These items serve as distinct icons of each group.

I am of the Shona tribe and my clan is the *Chiweshe*. The men are represented by the eland, a type of antelope, which we call *Mhofu* in Shona. Meanwhile, the women are known as *Chihera*. *Chihera* women are said to be fearless, forceful, and make things happen. While that stereotype is not true for some, I proudly identify with it. I am *Chihera*: I am fearless and forceful and make things happen. This is both despite and because of growing up in a patriarchal society that does not recognise and treat women as the equals of men.

Officially, this is not the case. According to the constitution of Zimbabwe, men and women are equal. However, even the law discriminates against women in many cases, such as legislation governing the conditions of part-time work and the fact that bride prices (*lobola*) still exist. Even the Supreme Court, in an inheritance dispute in 1999, ruled that women cannot be considered equal to men because of African cultural norms.

Thus, sadly, the standards of Zimbabwe do, often, discriminate against women. Men dominate as government representatives and civil servants, from the cabinet to the village and from ministries to district councils. Fortunately, this has been changing over the years with women occupying almost one-third of seats in the Zimbabwean parliament as of 2020.[2] But there is still a long way to go and a male-dominated society does not favour equal opportunities and treatment for women. Freehold landowners are predominantly men. And although women have succession rights, inheritance by widows and daughters is rare. Women are judged on their looks rather than their wits, and are often denied the opportunity to receive a full education, which most people require to make an impact on the world.

I, however, was fortunate. I was born of medium-income parents who supported me and instilled in me with strong values. Like the majority of households in Zimbabwe, ours was Christian. Christianity is the dominant faith in Zimbabwe[3] and my parents followed the traditional belief systems, like the Anglican Church (although I transitioned to the Pentecostal Church as I grew older).

And so, I learnt the importance of hard work and family values while staying true to myself, my potential, and my dreams. I played with building blocks and toy cars from the age of three. I built mock aeroplanes, television sets, and wire cars out of whichever materials my school friends and I found. I felt an adrenaline rush whenever I created something with my hands as a young girl, and then later, as a qualified engineer. And I am lucky to have parents who encouraged me to be myself every step of the way!

Unfortunately, not many girls get the same level of support. Cultural barriers and the lack of knowledge and exposure in engineering among women are disheartening. Many have their passion for engineering, or similar STEM (science, technology, engineering, maths) subjects shot down before they can take flight. Girls are told that engineering is a boy's profession by their parents or someone else they hold in high esteem, so they abandon the idea altogether.

Well, I am here to tell you that women are not only capable of being engineers. They can excel!

I am a *Chihera* woman by birth and an engineer by choice. Today, I am a civil, water, and sanitation engineer. My motto is "Making an impact in communities, one pipe at a time". I have witnessed the elation of the locals when water starts gushing out of taps and boreholes that I have helped put in place. I have cried tears of joy from witnessing people's livelihoods improve because they can access clean water. To live and not make an impact is, to me, a life wasted. I want to contribute something to the livelihood of current and future generations. And with my work, I can become a part of a broader agenda that is bigger than me. A generous initiative that gives purpose to my life and others. My profession allows me to bring hope where there was no hope; a beam of light where there was bleak darkness. By realising my dream to become an engineer, I am part of a movement that brings life-saving developments across cultures and borders, from Zimbabwe to Uganda, and Tanzania to France.

However, my mission goes beyond my skills as an engineer. I have seen the good I can do and, therefore, the good all women can do. So, in 2016, my vision to see more women in Africa take up positions of impact and influence in the engineering and science fields led me to start the Joy Makumbe Trust. The trust is dedicated to empowering women with entrepreneurial skills by offering support and career guidance workshops in schools, helping girls and their parents to interrogate and unlearn stereotypes that misinform families that girls cannot be engineers. I am living proof that such beliefs are not true, and it is my dream to inspire as many families as I can to support girls who have the desire to pursue STEM careers to be fearless and relentless about smashing down barriers. I had to do the same to make sure that my dream of becoming an engineer was not shattered by a society that insists that engineering is a man's profession; where girls are socialised to believe that there are feminine careers meant only for them and masculine ones meant only for boys.[4] It is nonsense and I want to prove it to you!

We know this is a cultural problem of our own making. Research shows that young girls graduate from high school full of confidence in themselves and their passions but, after studying or working a few years in a male-dominated environment, most of that self-confidence has evaporated.[5] This is because women lack female mentors or role models in the field who can show them how to survive and thrive. Statistics from 2017 show that less than 28% of professionals in STEM careers were women and, for every five male engineers, there was only one female engineer.[6] Thus, women already established in STEM careers need to do much more to act as role models for young girls in their communities. These young girls, both at home and school, hear whispers in their ear over and over that they are not good enough for science-based subjects or careers. Without a voice to counter this view, and with so many schools lacking effective career guidance, the girls are doomed to graduate with the belief that they are incapable. All they are left with is what the patriarchy tells them. And bear in mind, when we talk of the patriarchy, we are not just speaking about men, but a system that works to promote men and suppress women, which many women and children support, as well.

It is not surprising this view is prevalent. On television, and throughout media in general, men are portrayed as achievers in life, business, and tech careers, whilst women are groomed to take great care of themselves for the "ultimate prize", which is marriage. Women are taught not to be ambitious, and those who are are labelled rebels by both men and women, alike.

Well, I want to be that voice that helps girls realise they can be engineers, and awesome ones, too! That they can and should enjoy themselves while pursuing their passions and dreams. I have been on this tech journey for almost two decades now. I have faced my share of hurdles, from people wanting to discourage me from embarking on a STEM career to systems put in place to extinguish my light. But I resisted, not just because I was strong and determined, but because I had people who encouraged me and kept pushing me forward. Now it is my turn to do that for you!

The battle to prove one's worth is an ongoing one. You have to prove yourself every day. I want the young engineers to know that it is a journey full of obstacles, but we must, and we can, overcome them. I have navigated deep valleys, climbed high mountains, and I am still going strong. It is unimportant how many times you fall; only that you rise again.

Writing this book was a period of great reflection for me as I revisited important and defining events throughout my life, some of which were difficult to remember. Some events, which I had long ago forgotten, popped up because their contribution was necessary to create a complete and coherent book. It is not easy to lay yourself bare, but I have been as authentic as I can in telling everything as it happened, so that the readers can relate to my joys, frustrations, and pains. It is my fond hope you will take my experiences and lessons and use them to inspire your own journey, or support a family member or friend undergoing similar trials. If this will motivate someone, somewhere, to challenge oppressive beliefs and encourage women to pursue their own interests and careers, then it was a worthwhile journey for me to take.

INTRODUCTION

I n this book, I share my tech journey from birth to practising engineer. I highlight the situations and circumstances that helped shape my interest in STEM subjects throughout my childhood, academic career, and professional life, including stories from some different projects I have supervised and the people I have interacted with on this journey. Through sharing my tech girl stories and adventures, I will demonstrate how I learnt that it takes passion and drive to pursue a career in STEM as a woman.

It is my fond hope that this book will boost the confidence of girls and women everywhere, so that when they embark on their own journeys, they remember that it is a road travelled by someone who faced similar challenges and overcame them without losing her love for engineering. As a tech girl who knows the joy of serving and making a difference, especially while working in an industry dominated by men, it is my intention with this book to inspire girls and prove that their dreams need not be limited to so-called feminine careers.

As I embark on this tech mission, I hope to pique your curiosity and motivate you, dear reader. I want you to feel my hand take yours as you boldly take on the task of challenging traditional beliefs and discovering a new way, a new reality.

To the girls and women with ambitions to study and work in STEM careers, I challenge you to embrace your girl power. I want you to know that you are not alone. Together, we can overcome any barriers and emerge stronger and wiser on the other side. Using my own experiences as a template, I hope to help young girls understand that engineering can be a pathway to realising your dreams of helping and improving your community and the world at large. And to the junior engineers reading this, that it is possible to fight and overcome the obstacles at your workplace. I desire that, after reading this memoir, you will be motivated to chase your dreams and be unstoppable in your pursuit of them.

To the parents, relatives, and friends of these ambitious women, I want to show you the important part you have to play and how, so you can encourage the tech girls in your life to succeed and be happy. I will show you what is possible by telling my own story and explain how you can encourage their independence and drive.

Also, to the boys and men reading this book, I hope you discover the truth about men and women pursuing STEM careers: that girls are just as capable as boys. The idea that any career is meant for boys only is nonsense. By the time you read the last chapter, you will be not only more supportive of girls and women in your communities chasing their dreams, but you will discover how championing them will benefit your own ambitions and happiness, as well.

There is a long way on this journey towards equality between women and men, I know, but the train has left the station. A time is coming when all who are in positions of influence will show the girls in their circles that they believe in them, that they are capable and strong. We can help move the train along by challenging the patriarchal systems and beliefs in place and encouraging each other to fulfil our ambitions.

I do not cover in detail any aspects of engineering work in this book because it is not meant to be read as an engineering manual. Rather, this book is a tool to challenge, motivate, and inspire anyone with a hobby, interest, or goal in something that their community has told them they cannot or should not attempt, particularly women interested in STEM subjects and careers. If any engineering work is mentioned, it is only brief, to give some context to the events that transpired. Of course, the issues affecting women in patriarchal societies are diverse and many. In the interest of keeping this book concise and useful, I do not cover all these issues but have limited myself to those with a bias towards STEM. However, while many challenges described in this book concern my cultural upbringing in Zimbabwe, the core lessons apply to the vast majority of people and belief systems around the world.

CHAPTER 1

Born A Leader

"You can only have one FIRSTBORN child.
You may love all your children deeply
and with passion, but there is something
unique about the FIRSTBORN"

—Raymond E. Feist

Some people say leaders are made and, being the firstborn, I believe that I was catapulted into leadership straight from my mother's womb. It is not a position I chose, but one that I assumed, nonetheless, with all the responsibilities that came with it. In fact, it is such a common belief in Zimbabwean culture for the firstborn to take on the role of the leader that the subject regularly features in popular music. As a young girl, I remember being drawn to such songs and I would hum away whenever they played on the radio. The lyrics would often call for the firstborn to be courageous and determined, as they would have to face all of life's battles alone. So, my surroundings influenced by ambitious drive right from the beginning.

I also believe that I was meant to be an engineer. After all, my mother carried me for ten months, not the usual nine. As is the norm with all heavy equipment, it takes a little longer to make. Everything must be in place and at just the right specifications.

Our first family home was in Highfield, a residential suburb, south-west of Harare, the capital of Zimbabwe. My parents had been granted a house by the government soon after their wedding. The house was brick-under-tile with two bedrooms and it was fenced and gated. There was a garden for planting a row of vegetables behind the house, a piece of land reserved for flowers, and a lawn in the front. Being a high-density area, the houses were close to each other but far enough for private conversation inside your home. These particular houses were reserved for wedded couples and just the right size for new families.

When I asked my mother what I was like as a baby, she said, "You grew up like a cabbage in a well-watered garden. You did not bother me at all". My mother had been pleasantly surprised by this. While the other children in the surrounding houses were suffering from fevers due to one illness or another, I was busy playing with my toys or lying quietly on my baby blanket. My mother never had to take me to the doctor for any illness; only for the usual baby check-ups. I was a plump and healthy little girl, with round chubby cheeks, who ate almost everything that was set before her. I am fortunate that this is something I have carried with me into adulthood and passed on to my daughter, as well.

At age two, we moved from Highfield to an apartment in a neighbouring suburb called Glen Norah. Our apartment was located on the second floor of the building and, like Highfield, the zone was high-density. So, for my safety's sake, the first thing my father did was to show me how to walk up and down the stairs on my own, using the handrails as a guide. My parents feared, if left to my own devices, I would tumble down the stairs. Within no time, I was using those stairs like a pro and, once I was old enough, coming and going of my own at free will. I would disappear to my friend's apartment for hours on end. Tendayi lived on the ground floor and I would often visit to play or eat the delicious mealie-meal porridge mixed with peanut butter that Tendayi's mother liked very much to prepare.

At three, my mother found me scribbling the letters A and S on a piece of paper she had given me to write on. My parents always liked to keep me busy with paper and crayons. To this day, my mother says she does not know who taught me those letters. I am told my speech developed normally, and I was an intelligent child.

Despite my love of exploration and scribbling, I enjoyed my diverse toy collection. I had toy cars, building blocks, dolls, jigsaw puzzles, and countless colouring books. My father, particularly, liked to bring me toys that I had to figure out how to build by joining certain pieces together. I would sit there for hours trying to figure out how each one was done, trying out piece after piece until, finally, I would do it. The sense of achievement would illuminate my face as I rushed to show my parents what I had made.

My father encouraged curiosity in other ways, too. I had a shelf full of encyclopaedia books that he had bought for me. I loved flipping through the pages and gasping at all the incredible pictures that would pop out from the glossy pages. Many of the words were still too long and complex for me to understand at such a young age, but I enjoyed them, all the same. And from the moment I could comprehend some of the text, my father encouraged me to read at least two pages every day. Of course, some days were better than others when it came to sticking to that plan.

I enjoyed playing "House" with the dolls in my toy collection. I loved changing their clothes and doing their hair. There was, however, one doll above the rest: my baby, whom I named Rose. She was my favourite and I would take her everywhere with me. More than anything, I loved dressing her up and plaiting her long, black hair.

One day, I told my mother I wanted to shave Rose's hair so that new hair could grow, just like mine did. Of course, my mother warned me against this, trying to explain, as simply as possible, that Rose's hair and my hair were different. But this advice fell on deaf ears. What did she know? I knew what my baby needed, and she needed a haircut pretty badly! As soon as my mother was out of sight, I took the opportunity to carry out my deed without interference. I pulled out a pair of scissors from my mother's sewing bag and sat Rose firmly on my lap. *Snip, snip, snip* was the only sound that disturbed the calmness of that sunny afternoon as my young fingers performed their task. After a couple of minutes, I held Rose at arm's length and admired my handiwork. Minutes later, my mother walked back into the room to find Rose's hair in a black heap on the floor beside me and a bald Rose on my lap. She did not utter a word but went on as usual with her daily business. Every day after that, I would inspect my baby's hair for any sign of growth. I would even wash her head and apply the same oil I used after my bath. But nothing seemed to change. One week passed, one month, three months. Still, Rose remained bald. Eventually, the realisation hit me hard: Rose's hair would never grow again. I remember weeping for Rose's hair and asking her to forgive me.

Rose got lost along the way as we moved from house to house. I will forever treasure the good times we shared. And although I was horrified at the time, I think back on how my mother silently encouraged my own form of exploration and creativity with fondness.

As the firstborn of my parents' children, I was the most photographed baby of all my siblings. My father, being well-educated and a teacher, valued the importance of capturing memories. He owned a black-and-white camera that he used to document my childhood. He captured the day my mother and I were discharged from the hospital, although my face is hidden in the photo, so tightly wrapped am I in a woollen blanket and held close against my mother's chest, and images of me scribbling away with crayons or playing with my favourite toys. There are even photos of me modelling my latest hairdos; something I learnt to pose for from a very early age. Well, who can blame me? Wherever I went, the camera followed. My father recorded anything and everything I did.

I ate all flavours of food, went to esteemed kindergartens, had good clothes, and enjoyed exciting outings on most weekends. I was even the only child my father ever taught how to drive. Thus, I was the child of their youth; I was their firstborn, and I was deeply loved and supported at every opportunity.

Have you ever stopped to think about why we have so few girls in tech- or STEM-related roles? I was a curious child and enjoyed constructing things. I enjoyed playing with toy cars and building blocks. My mind was trained to be creative from a young age. These are just some of the skills which are required for most tech careers. And yet, many cultures dictate that boys play with toy cars and girls stick to dolls.[7] Parents, knowingly or otherwise, play a large part in reinforcing this stereotype early on. For instance, when girls want to play with the toy cars and boys with the dolls, parents silently cast a disapproving eye. However, if girls are to nurture their interest in STEM subjects as much as boys, they must be allowed to derive the same joy in making things using their hands from an early age. (Likewise, for our boys to be able to develop and show more emotion and empathy, let them have those dolls.) Dr Elizabeth Sweet, a sociologist lecturer at the University of California, says, "When we give both boys and girls equal choices from an early age, it logically follows that they will continue to expect and demand equality in their personal, social, and professional lives, and they will not see anything abnormal with that".

So, tech girls, be assertive and keep asking for what you want and need to ensure you fully explore the hobbies and skills that interest you.

And parents, are you willing to get your girls interested in tech by buying her tech-related toys? The best way to discover what your child enjoys and what they are good at is to give them a range of tools, so I invite you to consider buying a wide variety of toys for them, regardless of their sex.

Also, I encourage parents to cultivate a reading culture in all their children by buying those books that will raise their curiosity and spark their imagination. Develop in your children the discipline to make time each day to read at least a few pages from a book. They will not keep to this timetable like clockwork because they are just children, but you will sow in them a seed of discipline, an enjoyable interest, and a valuable skill that will last for life.

Ultimately, be willing to let your children discover things for themselves. Empower them to make their own decisions. As long as they don't hurt themselves, let them cut off that doll's hair to discover that it doesn't grow back; allow them to learn life lessons on their own. They will understand that you trust them enough to decide for themselves, while knowing that you are still nearby to support and protect them. This will boost their confidence in decision-making and they will understand that it is okay to make mistakes and that life must go on.

Summary of Lessons

- Provide your children with access to toys that require engineering or creative skills to increase their interest in STEM subjects later in life.
- Children who are encouraged to read will continue to do so as they grow.
- Children who have been empowered to make decisions demonstrate higher levels of confidence.

CHAPTER 2

Primary School Years

"Education is our passport to the future,
for tomorrow belongs to the people
who prepare for it today."

—*Malcolm X*

By the time I started primary school at the age of six, we had moved to Houghton Park, a middle-density suburb, south of Harare's city centre. After Zimbabwe won its independence in 1980, many African middle managers were given loans to buy houses in once white-only areas. My father met the criteria, so our family was one of the beneficiaries.

The houses were bigger and looked lovely with gardens of plush green grass and pretty flowers. I remember being excited because my parents had promised me my own bedroom. After all, the house had three bedrooms. It was neatly fenced and gated and had a small, one-bedroom cottage as an outbuilding. There was enough space for me to play with my friends and for my father to park his car. The icing on the cake was that I would be starting primary school at a local government school within walking distance, so I would not need my parents to take me each morning.

Primary school was competitive. I was not the only kid in my class who always wanted to receive the best grades in the hope of winning the coveted Book Prize at the end of the year. Specifically, this prize was eyed by a boy called Philip: my nightmare and rival. He was a constant thorn in my side. Any wrong answer in a maths test would cost me because Philip was certain to get it right. Throughout my primary school years, I remember the Book Prize fluctuating between Philip and myself.

In class, we sat in groups of six. Each group was determined by the academic performance of the individuals: group one comprised the highest performers; group six the lowest. To earn a place in group one, you had to deliver a consistently sterling performance. I worked hard to ensure an almost permanent seat in group one. Still, I remember my marks slipped one week and I was moved to group two; I did not like this at all. I had to pull up my socks in the next class to regain my seat. Besides, Philip had remained in group one and I distinctly remember his smug grin when our teacher read out the names for each group that week. When I got home, I ranted and raved to my parents, who listened to every wail attentively.

After I finished venting, my dad asked, very calmly, "So why do you think you did not meet the mark?"

"Well," I stammered, "my maths mark was not very good."

"Why is that? What was the problem?" my dad asked.

"I do not understand vectors. I get confused," I replied.

For the next hour, my father took me through the textbook chapter on vectors. You see, my father is a science graduate from the University of Zimbabwe, then called the University of Rhodesia. He had studied maths and chemistry and worked as a teacher before moving into the food industry. With his support and encouragement, I quickly made my comeback to group one. I had wanted to give up on maths entirely, but my father showed me that there are many ways to approach a problem to find the answer; you just need to find the method that works for you. I remember how proud of myself I felt; I had put in the extra work and it had paid off. Best of all, mathematics became so much fun for me after learning this lesson.

But my father's advice went beyond specific subject problems. He taught me that to achieve good grades regularly, I needed to be disciplined and organised. He would encourage me to draft a timetable to remind me what I needed to do and when. I even included my playtime in the timetable, when I would go out with my friends to catch grasshoppers or butterflies.

Beyond arming me with the tools and responsibility to succeed in my studies, my parents would check in with how I was doing. Besides the annual Book Prize, our primary school teachers awarded us merit badges every Friday for various achievements. If I went too long without bringing home a merit badge, my parents would ask if I was having any problems at school. It was not that I was facing any difficulties, per se; rather, the competition was so stiff. I would mumble something about how some boy had got the badge and I would try to get it next week. However, I could see the expectation in my parents' faces, so I, too, would expect nothing less than the best from myself. It was a heavy weight on my shoulders as a child and I did not always understand why they pushed me this hard. Naturally, I would sometimes resent all this pressure. But as I grew older, I felt grateful that they had because it helped mould me into the ambitious and successful woman I am today.

My new approach to learning was put to the test in grade seven when we took exams in maths and English. Like our class groups, the exams were graded such that one unit was the highest score and nine was the lowest. Thus, a grade of two units indicated a one in maths and a one in English. The day I left home that morning to write these exams, my father bid me farewell and said, "Go and get your two units". I remember feeling both excited and scared that he believed I could get top marks. Was I ready? Had I prepared adequately to get that score? I had to breathe in and out deeply to steady myself as I headed for school.

Well, I was not prepared to disappoint my parents, who believed in me so much. So, you know what? Two units are exactly what I got! My mother and father believed that I could do it, so I pushed myself. They believed in their little girl when generally girls were seen as non-performers. Girls were considered poor in mathematics because it was a "boy's subject".

But the idea of the maths brain—that the woman's brain is not as capable as performing mathematical computations as male brains—is a myth, and a rather destructive one at that. In fact, research shows no innate cognitive biological differences between men and women in maths.[8]

Yet, perpetuating the myth is enough to cause great harm. Many girls lose confidence in maths by the third grade because the teachers, parents, and boys around them keep telling them that they will be poor at the subject. Boys, on the other hand, are told again and again that they are strong in maths. Girls carry this belief with them throughout their lives, so do not attempt to study the same subjects as boys by the time they reach higher education.

Well, I had squashed that myth by excelling in mathematics and getting a first-class grade in the exam. I proved girls were just as capable. All I needed was the same support from an early age that the boys received and my parents had given that to me.

Shelley Correll, a professor of sociology at Stanford University, summarises the maths brain myth rather concisely: "Boys do not pursue mathematical activities at a higher rate than girls because they are better at mathematics. They do so, at least in part, because they think they are better."

To the parents and teachers, I invite you to encourage girls to work hard in STEM subjects to achieve the same grades as boys. Tell them they are just as capable. Instead of dismissing their struggles as an inability to master the subject, help them find new ways to understand problems and concepts the same way you would a boy.

On the other hand, do not overburden every boy. Many boys suffer from the huge pressure put on them by their parents and teachers to be great at maths. Some of these boys struggle with the subject and that's okay. They simply need to be encouraged as well, if they are to improve.

Remember: it is not about boys being better at maths than girls. It is simply that some children are better at certain subjects than others, and all kids need encouragement to improve.

Of course, as I have mentioned, I was not without my own pressures. My parents never hid their expectation of me to set the pace for my siblings. Firstborn children in Zimbabwe are not only expected to be exemplary at school but also at home. Refuse to eat something, for example, and you could expect to hear your mother yelling from the kitchen, "Don't you start. Do you want your brothers and sisters not to eat, as well?"

This was true for me. Despite being a good eater in general, I remember I hated the slimy texture of okra and I would always lose my appetite when I had to eat it. But the minute I asked for something else instead, my siblings would chime in that they didn't want to eat okra, either. My mother would give me the eye, which promised me punishment if I continued to defy her: a long unblinking stare and a stone-faced expression. It only took one glance and I would settle down to eat, swallowing quickly to minimise the slimy experience.

Likewise, if one of my younger brothers or sisters came home with a grazed knee or in tears, I was expected to relay every detail of what had happened to my mother. "How am I supposed to know?" I would sometimes say. "I wasn't even there!"

When I was in grade four, my young sister fell while racing up and down the neighbourhood streets. I had not been present at the time as I had visited my friend Abigail's house to see her new doll. I arrived home to find my sister snivelling as my mother cleaned her knee. My mother asked me what had happened to her. I started to explain that I had been at Abigail's house, only to be cut short with a retort that I was neglecting my duties of looking after my siblings.

As you can imagine, these expectations start to engrave themselves into one's subconscious: that you must protect your siblings and that your siblings look up to you. You are taught that your siblings depend on you and you should not let them down. Although it was difficult at times, I adopted this role proudly and earned my parents' confidence.

By the time I was in grade five, my parents trusted me enough to take my siblings to play soccer a few streets away. It was a bright day as we ventured out to play and everyone knew everybody because we all went to the same school, so the atmosphere was relaxed and happy. Before we started playing, we all removed our shoes and lined them up by the gate. Another boy had bruised his toes previously because of the shoes he had worn, and we wanted to avoid the same fate. There were squeals of laughter as we played and shrieks of disbelief when someone failed to score. And there were also yelps of pain because playing barefoot was not as comfortable as we'd hoped (we were aged between nine and eleven and didn't know any better). But overall, we had the time of our lives running up and down the yard, kicking up the surrounding dust.

Of course, we had to call it a day at some point. Sweating and panting, we ran towards the gate to collect our shoes before heading home. Only, when we got to the gate, our shoes were nowhere to be seen. Eventually, we realised that they must have been stolen and the worry of what this meant could be seen on every young face. My siblings looked at me, their eyes mirroring my fear over how we would explain this to our parents. Begrudgingly, we made our way home, the hotter-than-usual tarmac adding insult to injury.

When we arrived, the first thing my mother noticed was our bare feet, then the dusty ankles, then our forlorn faces.

"Why are you walking barefoot?" she asked. The question was directed to me. I explained what had happened, and she looked at me in disbelief. "How can you be so trusting as to leave your shoes outside the gate unattended? I expected better judgement from you as the oldest. Now, all your siblings' shoes have been stolen. I am not going to buy you any new tackies any time soon." We left the room with my mum's eyes downcast. A perfect day was ruined. Because of my poor judgement, I had cost us our shoes.

Being a young child learning the expectations on my shoulders, this was not my only mistake. Our teachers would set homework every day, except for Fridays, and my mother expected me to supervise my siblings to ensure they did it. One day, when the weather was particularly nice, my siblings asked me if they could do their work while sitting outside in the sun. Well, I saw nothing wrong with that and I agreed. They laid out a mat on the concrete paving in our backyard and got to work. I sat with them as I read a book.

After some time, our phone started ringing. My mother and father had stepped out of the house, so I dashed inside to answer it. It was my friend, Abigail. We could talk for hours about anything and everything without my parents to police my time on the phone, so I made myself comfortable on the sofa and chatted away. We must have talked for almost an hour, only hanging up when Abigail's mother yelled at her to get off the phone. I stood up, stretched like a Cheshire cat, and made my way back outside.

The sight that greeted me sent a chill down my spine. The whole concrete paving was littered with loose paper and my siblings were nowhere to be seen. They had finished their homework and disappeared like a mirage in the desert, leaving everything out there on the mat. Our three puppies had decided to take over and play tug of war with the books, shaking them like juicy bones. I was dumbstruck. I managed to croak the puppies' names as I dashed forward to salvage what I could, but the damage was done. With shaky fingers, I collected what remained of the books and waited for my mother's return. I felt like someone waiting for the death penalty.

As soon as I heard the gate creak, I went to meet my mother before she could enter the house. Immediately, I burst into tears, partly as a ploy to seek mercy and partly because I was scared of my impending punishment. Our parents rarely beat us, but the constant threat of it meant we were always afraid. Through the tears, I managed to describe what had happened. I told her that I knew I should have been watching them and that I was sorry. My mother did not answer, she just turned, walked towards a peach tree we had in our compound, and broke off a thin branch. I waited, immobilised by fear and uncertainty, not knowing whether I should run or just stand there like a statue. My mother grabbed hold of my hands in a vice-like grip and gave me a thorough beating on my legs. All I could focus on was the motion of her hand going up and down and the sharp stings of pain shooting up my legs. As I continued to cry, I lay down on the ground, begging for forgiveness, wriggling my body from left to right, trying to avoid the stick. After what seemed like an eternity, my mother stopped and entered the house.

I lay there for a while, willing the pain to subside, the words *I should have been watching them* repeating in my head. I had lost my focus in this instance as a leader and it had cost me. With leadership comes great responsibility, and I vowed to never lose focus again.

We all feel pressure and weight on our shoulders, but your responsibilities are yours alone to bear and manage. I would feel fearful about messing up and letting my parents down, so I learnt to be sensible and prioritise my time. Sometimes, I would forego playing with my friends to watch over my siblings. I hated such days because I wanted to go out and play; I wanted to be a child who did not always have to watch every step they took was an exemplary one. Being the firstborn was certainly bittersweet, but the responsibility I learnt at home prepared me for responsibility at school. I knew how to take charge and lead the class in work or during sports activities.

All this, my focused studying and my lessons at home, culminated in me achieving great success at school. I was nominated for class representative one year, then prefect the next, and, finally, deputy head girl in my last year.

Summary of Lessons
- Girls are as capable of excelling in mathematics as boys.
- Boys must not be pressured into excelling in mathematics just because they are boys.

- Girls and boys must be encouraged to work hard in all subjects. When parents and teachers support children, they excel in their academic studies.
- Trust children with responsibilities and hold them to account (reward achievement and effort and punish neglect). This will prepare them for responsibilities later in life.

CHAPTER 3

The Power of Home Influence

"Parents are the ultimate role models for children.
Every word, movement, and action has an effect.
No other person or outside force has a greater
influence on a child than the parent."

—*Bob Keeshan*

As parents, we influence how our children relate to others. It all begins with the home environment.

I made a lot of friends in primary school, both boys and girls. Some kids lived in our neighbourhood while others came from neighbouring suburbs. So, besides getting together at break time to share sandwiches and drinks, I would hang out with some of them after school. We enjoyed playing house and often imitated what we saw in our respective homes.

I remember one particular day playing house with my friend, John. He played the role of the father and I played the mother. I asked John to come and help me with the cooking. He looked at me with utter disgust and told me that it was a woman's job. John was only eight! I argued with him that anyone could cook because I had seen both men and women cooking on television. Besides, my brothers always prepared something for themselves when they got home from school. John grunted back at me that his father had told him it was only women who did the household chores. At his house, only his mother and his two sisters did the cleaning and cooking. I was annoyed by this comment. Surely, as long as you have hands, you could cook? I asked John if he had ever seen men cooking on TV, but he would not budge from his argument.

John had inherited his rigid attitude towards gender roles from his father. Similarly, I inherited my flexible attitude from my own family. This is common, as children usually form their ideas about gender flexibility from what they see in their own home. For example, households with fewer women tend to be more flexible because the men must assume a larger selection of chores.[9]

However, it shouldn't depend on how many women live in a household for men to be more open to interchangeable gender roles. As parents, I invite you to be more flexible in the way you allocate tasks to your children, regardless of how many boys or girls live in the household. Reinforce in your children what they are capable of achieving, stressing that they can be anything they want to be in this world.

This goes for careers, too. One afternoon, as my friends and I were sat licking ice creams with satisfied cat grins on our faces, we started to discuss the careers we wanted to follow when we were older. My friends chorused that they wanted to be teachers, pilots, doctors, and nurses. I remember saying I wanted to be an engineer (I had been watching a programme on television about engineers the previous day and was feeling inspired). Everyone turned to stare at me and asked me what an engineer did. I tried to explain as much as I could (my knowledge was limited at the time), so I described a scene of engineers laying huge water pipes and celebrating when water started gushing out of the taps.

"Is that not a man's job? It seems to be hard," said John. John again!

"No," I answered, smugly. "I can be anything that I want."

This prompted a debate about why only men could do the job because they are stronger than women, and that women must only be nurses or teachers, etc. My friends and I parted without any goodbyes or smiles.

That night, I discussed this issue with my mother and father, who reiterated I could pursue whatever career I desired. That gave me confidence and I remember I went to bed content that night. Who cared what John, James, or Samuel thought or said? I could be anything that I wanted to be because my parents said so!

Another explanation for the belief that gender roles are fixed is that patriarchal societies portray men as the dominant sex who should lead and assume positions of power. Thus, when women assume "masculine" roles, some men feel threatened or embarrassed. The male ego is dented if these women perform better than them. These men become hostile and resentful and will look for ways to frustrate women.

To the parents reading this, which parents do you identify with: John's or mine? Of course, it could be you identify with John's parents. But, if so, I challenge you to consider whether your ideas are based on logic or because you were taught them. Perhaps you were brought up in a patriarchal culture or a household where gender roles were fixed and defined. Men are capable of cooking (some of the best chefs in the world are men) and I am living proof women can be successful engineers. Times are changing. More women are now taking up roles traditionally considered to be only suitable for men, and they are doing a great job. So, perhaps gender roles aren't as fixed as you thought? For the sake of the tech girls in your life, I hope you consider this question seriously.

The same goes for boys, of course. Quite often in patriarchal societies, boys who want to pursue traditionally "feminine" roles are usually dissuaded or forbidden from doing so by their parents because they consider it embarrassing. Any son that insists on pursuing their passion is likely to end up without any support from the parents, financially, emotionally, or otherwise.

Humans are social beings who care a lot about what people in their community say or think about them. Sadly, this means parents, teachers, and friends sometimes would rather force a boy or man to do something they don't want to do, so they don't feel embarrassed or ashamed. But the cost of the pressures we mount on our fathers, husbands, brothers, and sons to pursue the careers and interests we regard as manly can lead to depression and even suicide.[10],[11]

However, the pressure parents put on their children is not always limited to gender roles. As well, they feel they must raise the star child, who will only have the opportunity to succeed in the modern world if they excel at everything the parent considers important. But this kills their child's passions and removes any element of choice. Meanwhile, other parents have their hearts set on their kids following in their footsteps or fulfilling a family dream. There is nothing wrong with encouraging kids to try new things. It is part of a parent's responsibility to expose their children to various opportunities and to ask them to be willing to try something brand new, even if their child offers resistance. But do not deny your children their childhood, nor forbid them from trying things that interest them, or you will kill their creativity and happiness.

By paying attention to your children, you can help them fine-tune or broaden their interests; whichever is appropriate. When kids follow their passions, it's amazing what can happen. This is how greatness is born.

Summary of Lessons

- The home environment is extremely important in shaping children's beliefs.
- Parental support is necessary if children are to try new things and stick with them.
- Stereotyping roles disadvantages children from finding and following their passions.

CHAPTER 4

I Am Not Weak

"I always believe I can beat the best,
achieve the best. I always see myself
in the top position."

—*Serena Williams*

Michael was a bully in my fifth-grade class with no regard for anyone else. What he wanted he got. What he said was to be obeyed. When he asked you to jump, you had to ask how high, not why. For reasons best known only to Michael, he did not like me, and the time came that we would clash.

One day, while I was on my way to the front of the classroom to sharpen my pencil with the huge pencil sharpener fastened to the teacher's desk, I stepped on him by accident (or, perhaps, he put his foot in the way deliberately). Whatever the case, it quickly became apparent he would not accept my apologies. He looked me straight in the eye and said, in a hushed voice, "See you at home time".

I knew what that meant. That meant a thorough beating I would not forget in a hurry.

The day grew dim and hazy for me after that. I could not concentrate.

I could hear the teacher's voice, but she seemed distant, like she was tucked away in a bottle. What was I going to do? I had never fought anyone in my life, nor was I accustomed to taking a beating. I worked hard not to displease my teachers by maintaining good grades and I stayed out of mischief at home as much as possible to avoid my parents' rod. The thought of having pain inflicted on my body made me want to pass out. I consoled myself that it was all a joke and Michael would forget about the whole incident before we were dismissed for the day. But I was wrong!

I found Michael waiting for me about fifty metres from the school gate, surrounded by his loyal supporters, who were there to witness my beating. I tried to portray some confidence, so I squared my shoulders and picked up speed, hoping to pass by without an incident. However, he blocked my route and left me nowhere else to go. I felt a sharp jab at my shoulder the moment I was beside him. In a thick, gruff voice, he spat, "I told you I would be waiting for you". My heart was pounding so hard, I thought they could all see my chest going up and down. All the other students started shouting for Michael to get on with it, mostly just so that they could go home. Children can be so innocent even when they are mean.

I felt more jabs at my back, now with increased pressure and urgency. And then, I lost it! I felt a deep rage rise from the pit of my stomach and burn its way up my throat. I felt Michael was all in my face because I was a girl and an easy target for him. He was a big boy in stature and had picked on me because he thought I was weak and a walkover. In my fury, I swung around so quickly that Michael was caught off guard. Whether it was my swift swing or the angels watching over me, Michael missed a step and went tumbling to the ground.

I charged at him like a bull seeing red. Tears blurred my vision, but I could see my target just fine. I jumped on top of him like a rider jumping on a horse and started pounding away with both hands. I punched him with all the rage I felt for being accused of a crime I didn't commit and with the anger I felt from being bullied and belittled. Michael lay there, trying to ward off my blows. Eventually, I felt myself being lifted. I was still kicking and lashing out viciously, all the while sobbing uncontrollably. It was two of my friends that broke up the fight, after which they slowly and silently walked me home. Before I entered the house, I wiped away my tears and blew my nose, determined to keep the fight hidden.

Later that day, I was sitting in our lounge, freshly bathed and ready to watch my favourite Pink Panther cartoons on our black and white television. There was a knock on the door and in walked Michael with his mother (they only lived three houses from ours). My heart skipped a beat as I looked at Michael, though he would not cast even a glance in my direction. His mother greeted my own with civility.

"I have come to ask about something my son has told me. He says that one of your children beat him up on their way home from school today?" Michael's mother then turned to him and said, "Have you seen the boy anywhere?" Michael slowly lifted a limp hand and pointed in my direction. His mother cast a swift glance at me and exclaimed, "What! A girl!" She gave her son one loud clap on the cheek, apologised to my mother, and left our house, pulling Michael behind her.

My mother asked me what had transpired and I described everything that had happened.

"Well, it is not good to fight at school," she said after taking it all in. "But in this instance, I see you were defending yourself."

I am proud I was strong and defended myself that day. Physical aggression should be avoided as much as possible and it often means getting ragged and dirty in the process. But the fight made me realise that I should not let others walk over me just to boost their ego and because of my sex. I realised that I had to stand up for myself and my beliefs if I wanted to be taken seriously or treated with respect. This lesson became the foundation of how I would carry myself throughout my professional life: I was not weak but strong, and I could defend my own.

Incidentally, that was the first and only fistfight I ever got involved in my entire life.

Michael was not the first boy to assume girls are weak. I believed I was weak, too, because that's how people treated me. I was expected to be frail and act fragile all the time. When I visited my grandmother, she would stop me from lifting pieces of wood or other bric-a-brac lying around the compound. She would shout things like, "Leave that, you cannot lift it. You will hurt yourself. You are not a boy. Your brothers will pick it up." And she'd reprimand me when my siblings and I played physical games, like climbing trees or racing around the compound like a wheelbarrow. Those games required power and energy, so they were considered boys' games. Not that we listened to her. As soon as we noticed grandmother's eye stray for a while, we were back at them. But my grandmother wasn't the only one to promote this world-view and it took a fight to show me that I was stronger than everyone said.

To my tech girls, do you perceive yourself as weak when confronted by obstacles that seem insurmountable? Trust me, you are stronger than you think, both in body and mind. Don't let the bullies of this world intimidate you. Know you are as good or better than them and let that confidence fuel your actions.

People take advantage of women every day because they believe they are the weaker sex and cannot challenge them. The car mechanic may try to get away with a half-done job because he believes you do not have the know-how to challenge him. An estate agent may try to charge you more when selling you a house because they think women don't have the acumen to deal with property issues. Girl, challenge them all. You have what it takes to fight it out and win. And if you don't win one battle, you will live to fight another day and grow wiser and stronger for the next one.

And remember, being strong and defending yourself is not something you need always do alone. There is no shame in asking for help and there is strength in numbers, so seek the assistance you need, whatever the situation.

This goes for men, too! Patriarchal societies encourage men to bottle up their emotion or to feel like a failure if they cannot perform a "masculine" responsibility as expected. This leads to anger and frustration, which manifest as bitterness and resentment towards others (often those closest to them). Let us allow our men to show moments of vulnerability because they, too, are human.

If we can all acknowledge each other's strength and potential, work together to support one another, and accept that we should not be expected to do everything alone, we can all feel happier and more fulfilled.

Incidentally, Michael and I went our separate ways after primary school. We were never friends but we would occasionally bump into each other years later and exchange pleasantries. No one ever mentioned the fight again, but I sincerely hope it did something to change his perception of women and that he treated them with respect thereafter.

Summary of Lessons

- A person's gender should not be a limiting factor to anything anyone sets out to do.
- Always stand up for yourself and what you believe is right.
- You are stronger than you think.
- Men should not expect or be pressured to believe they are infallible. They can be vulnerable and still be men.

CHAPTER 5

The Young Engineer

"Creativity is intelligence having fun."

—Albert Einstein

M ost school holidays, my father would take my siblings and me to his childhood home in the rural areas of Seke, a communal area about forty kilometres from Harare, to stay with his mother, my grandmother, so that we could enjoy a break from the city. I not only loved to see my grandmother, but also my cousins, who usually visited for the holidays, as well. We always embarked on such wonderful adventures and mischief together.

Like my parents, my grandmother was a woman who encouraged me to be a better version of myself. Every time we fulfilled some chore for her, like fetching water, she would recite some poetry to show her appreciation, which I later learnt was a common act among the people of the *Mhofu* totem whenever someone wanted to thank you for a job well done. The words of the poem were of adoration and praise. They spoke of how great one was: how they were achievers, unbeatable at what they did, and much appreciated.

When you are appreciated and shown you matter, you will not let anyone treat you as anything less. You feel great, so you continue to do positive acts that garner more appreciation, right? I knew I mattered and my grandmother would continue to bring out the best in me by encouraging the development of my attitude and skills. So, I learnt to challenge myself to be better at whatever I focused my attention on than I had been the previous day. I knew that mediocrity did not cut it and that one needs to keep working hard to achieve perfection.

As parents, the words we say to our children can make or break them. Words are powerful. These are but words on a page, yet they can transport you to my childhood or convey an important philosophy. Are we parents showing our children that they matter to us? We should sow positive seeds in our girls from a young age to boost their confidence and self-esteem and give them the strength of character to stand up for themselves in their lives and careers. When they know they matter, they will not accept anything less than they deserve. They will reject the people who tell them they are not good enough and prove them wrong.

My engineering exposure started there, on the golden sands of rural Seke. My cousins and I used to make model aeroplanes out of dried maize stalk leaves and pieces of grass. We used the grass to pierce a steady hole in the leaf, torn and shaped into a rectangle. Both the grass and the leaf had to have the right dimensions, else the leaf (the rotor) would not rotate or the plane would not fly. It was heart-breaking when we got the measurements wrong, but thrilling when the planes would fly, dancing in the wind, moving so fast that all we could see were blurred objects spinning around in circles. Unknown to us, we team of eight- and nine-year-old boys and girls had just experienced our first taste of complex engineering design and construction.

When our escapades took us indoors, we would sometimes settle down to construct our own television set, bringing every magazine within reach to the worktable and helping ourselves to one of grandmother's cardboard boxes. We would cut a jagged hole into one side of the box using a kitchen knife (we didn't have any scissors) and someone would tear up the pictures we needed from the magazines once we had decided what we would "watch" on TV. We then took it in turns changing the pictures that we displayed through the hole. And just like that, we had our own television set.

When that too got boring, we would look around for soft wires to build a moving car. We needed lots of wire for the project, so we would comb the whole compound and leave no stone unturned. Once we had a large enough heap, we got to work, tying each wire to the next, binding them together until our car started to take shape. We even built a working axle and wheels, so we could steer left and right.

The best thing about our engineering projects at grandmother's house was how everyone was involved in their own way, whether by tying wires together, preparing materials, or just by cheering on the others. Quarrels often broke out about who could control the finished project next and the older boys and girls had to work hard to maintain order in the group, but we would soon be squealing with enjoyment again in no time. It was great fun and we would often play until the encroaching night robbed us of our light. Finally, we would retire to grandmother's hut where the aroma of our supper cooking on the fire filled the air.

My young mind had already started to think technically about the mechanism of gadget construction and operation, and the support and praise of my grandmother and cousins provided me with a positive environment to explore and develop this intuitive interest.

Summary of Lessons

- Children enhance their creativity when they build things with their hands and make them work.
- Words have the power to make or break children.
- Generously showing love and care to children boosts their confidence and self-esteem.

CHAPTER 6

High School Years

"Educated girls become educated women who
have the knowledge, skills, and opportunity to play
a role in governance and democratic processes and
to influence the direction of their societies."

—*The Forum for African Women Educationalists (FAWE)*

started boarding at St David's Bonda Secondary School when I was
thirteen. I went to the same one as my mother and I remember asking
her to describe it. She told me the school was located in a valley with
mountains surrounding it. In the early morning, they would be capped
with white clouds, then the slopes would transform green by mid-morning,
forming a bright and enticing picture for the students watching from the
classrooms. She spoke of going for walks along the long, winding paths
which were lined with trees and wildflowers on either side. If you were
lucky, you could spot an occasional rabbit scurrying away from your ap-
proaching feet. I fell in love with this picture and I fell in love with the
school. I had to be a part of such beauty.

Sadly, my first impressions of the school were not as flowery as the
pictures I had formed in my head. The scenery was everything my mother

had described, but I had not expected to see such old school buildings and the grounds were covered in cow dung (the only cow dung I had seen previously was in the rural areas near my grandmother's home, although never close to her house). My heart sank because I had expected so much more and found myself wanting nothing else than to return home. I did not think I would survive in such a place.

It got even worse. The beds in the dormitories were small and hard, with a wafer-thin foam mattress. I was horrified and had to fight back the tears. The only thing that stopped me from clinging to my parents so they would take me back home with them was the fact that I had to act like the big girl they said I now was by starting high school. Primary school was long gone. I had to be strong. So, with my chin held high, I looked around at the other girls. Well, they seemed to be handling the situation quite well, so I decided to follow suit. I would not let these sour sights break my spirit.

Fortunately, a place does grow on you! After a month, I was comfortable and starting to love the school. I loved the beautiful scenery and evergreen vegetation on the undulating slopes. And I especially enjoyed how the mountains emerged from behind the thick morning mist to poke their noses towards bright blue skies later in the day, just as my mother had described. It was all rather breathtaking.

Have you ever been so blinded by your first impressions that you failed to appreciate something wonderful? You are not alone. I was so used to the level plains of Harare and Seke that it took me a while to see the beauty in the mountains. As I became familiar with the school buildings, they did not seem so old anymore. And as for the cows, I never saw them again after that first day. They did not live there and had probably just strayed onto the school premises because no one had been staying there at the time.

Before long, I was enjoying every minute of my high school experience. I loved going on weekend walks with my classmates and I made awesome friendships with girls from all walks of life, united by a common desire for knowledge. High school was a step up from primary school, but we supported each other in our studies and we all pushed each other hard.

There was no way you could slack off as no one would allow it. Likewise, the teachers drove us hard in our class exercises and with regular tests, and the headmaster reminded us often that we were expected to achieve top grades in our exams. It became our motto that "Bonda girls only represented excellence". It was push, push, push all the way, but we loved it. We literally burnt the midnight candle so many nights that we were sometimes punished for sneaking torches into bed to do extra reading.

Although I went to a boarding school, I still received support and guidance from my parents. Every year, the school hosted a visiting day when my parents would come and take a look at my books, talk to my teachers about my progress, and bring me lots of tuck and pocket money.

To the parents reading this, perhaps you have children at boarding school and there have been times when you have wished not to attend a visiting day? Let me explain by way of example why it is so important to go.

One year, when I was in Form Two, I was waiting with the other students in the car park as parents started to arrive. Each girl took it in turns to yelp with excitement as she recognised her parent's vehicle. Meanwhile, my eyes continued to dart up and down in a vain effort to find my mother and father's car. Three hours went by and the traffic of new arrivals began to dwindle. I remember I started to cry and became desperate to find somewhere private where I could wallow in my grief. Where were they? I thought they loved me and wanted to support me! They could not even leave Harare for one day and spare a few hours with me? My legs felt heavy as I rose and slowly made my way back to our dormitory.

But as I trudged along, head bowed low, looking at my feet, I heard a girl yell that a bus was pulling into the school. I was wary about getting my hopes up because my father had told me they would be driving to the school. Nonetheless, I dashed back to the car park just as some parents began to alight the bus.

Then, I saw them! I burst into tears as I pushed my way forward through the bodies of excited girls and ran straight into my father's arms.

They had come after all! They had not forgotten about me. My father hugged me back and explained how they had had some car trouble a few days earlier, so they had to take the bus, instead.

I still feel the joy in my heart that these two people had taken the time to visit me. I took my parents to my classroom, where all my books were neatly laid out on my desk for them to see. They went through each book and shook my hand or gave me a pat on the back where I had scored highly. Where I was struggling, they encouraged me to seek help from my teacher or friends. My father also promised to help me with my work during the holidays, which he did. The day ended well and my love for my parents was immeasurable.

Other girls slept through the day because no one came to visit them. I felt sorry for them. Every child needs someone to tell them that they are proud of their progress and achievements in school. Making their parents and loved ones proud is how many children fuel themselves for the rest of the school term, to maintain their good grades or up their game.

Parents, never underestimate the power your actions and words have to help your children feel supported and valued. Children push themselves harder to attain good grades if they believe it will make their parents happy and proud. I am a mother now and I always work hard to support my daughter in her school activities. Whenever she had a school play or dance, I made sure to attend, clap, and take pictures. And receiving this encouragement inspired her to ask for parts in school plays or dances because she knew I would come and watch her. On sports days, I cheered her on in her races. I have seen her face light up and her legs work harder at the sound of my piercing voice urging her to keep going. Even if I was very busy on parent-teacher days, I would dash to the school from work, go through some books and talk to my daughter's teachers (who feel more motivated to support your child when they know you are on this journey together), and then dash back to the office.

Are you taking the time to be there for your children and support their school activities? Are you showing them the support and care that will propel them forward every day? I understand that life is tough and society keeps many parents very busy making money to support their families, but please remember that not everything can be bought. Sometimes, all it takes to show your love is a pat on the back and the words, "I am proud of you".

Some of you tech girls might not have parents or guardians that support you as mine did me. Sometimes, they might disagree with your subject or career choices. Some may even threaten to stop paying your school fees if you defy them. As children, we all want to please and honour our parents. And we want them to be proud of us. But you owe it to yourself, your ambition, and your future happiness to chase your dreams. It takes strength to tell parents what we want, but it is worth it for the future you deserve.

And you don't have to face this challenge alone. School parents' and teachers' associations are available to intervene in such circumstances. The teachers will take it upon themselves to support their students' decisions and try to educate parents on the benefits of allowing girls to study the subjects they choose, including science and maths. So, if you know you are good at science subjects, for example, and your parents are not willing to let you pursue them, talk to your teachers to engage your parents on your behalf.

Summary of Lessons
- Support from the parent and teacher is vital for the success and confidence of every child.
- In the absence of supportive parents, students should approach their teachers, friends, and mentors for help and guidance.

CHAPTER 7

The Road To University

"It's important for us to engage with children
from a young age to ensure they grow up
to know that both boys and girls have a
place in STEM subjects"

—*Laura Giddings, STEM Education Manager, Northern Europe*

After writing my O-levels, I enjoyed a long school break whilst waiting for the results. I got tired of sitting at home all day watching television and reading books. I needed something more stimulating to keep me busy. So, I asked my father for a job at his company, which ran a programme for employees' children looking for work experience.

That is how I found myself at my father's factory on an early Monday morning. Little did I know, this particular day would have a significant bearing on my future career.

A human resources representative would address us new-hires and arrange for our department assignments. The areas with open positions were the canteen, marketing, human resources, engineering, packaging, accounts, and quality control. My father was the head of the Quality Control Department, but I knew I wanted to try something else. As we waited for the human resources representative to arrive, I saw a truck pass by with some huge pumps in the trunk before disappearing behind some buildings. I could see men in overalls with the word "Engineering" written on the back. They had each been holding toolboxes or various pieces of equipment that piqued my interest. When the representative arrived, I opted to work in the Engineering Department.

I was taken to the stores to dress in safety clothing. My overalls completely swallowed me up, despite being the smallest size available. And the safety shoes were thick and heavy (I later learnt they were capped with iron to protect your toes from falling objects). Afterwards, I spoke to the head of the engineering department, who assigned me to assist a team of men. My heart was pounding with expectation and excitement, although I admit I was also afraid I would prove to be a nuisance and of no help.

That same day, our team was called in because some boilers had failed to start. We had to work quickly to repair them or else risk spoiling a key resource. My team worked hard that day and I helped by handing over the tools as they were needed, giving me an opportunity to learn their names and uses. After a few hours, the boilers kicked into life and operations could resume.

This was the day that spelt it out for me. I wanted a job that had meaning and created impact. We had saved the company thousands of dollars by fixing the equipment in time and saving a resource from being thrown away. I wanted such an important job, an exciting job, a challenging job. On that day, I fell in love with engineering and I never looked back.

As much as I loved my high school, I wanted to study my A-levels at Gokomere Secondary School because of its students' high rate of success at passing science subjects with flying colours. Changing schools at this point was tricky because a new school was only likely to take you if you scored highly in your exams, while your current school would accommodate you even with average results. So, when the O-level results were finally released and I discovered that I'd scored A's in all my subjects, I was thrilled and I knew I was certain to attend Gokomere.

However, my confidence was short-lived. The day my offer letter arrived, I discovered it was for an A-level placement in Bonda, not Gokomere. I could not understand what had happened. Why did Gokomere not select me? I burst into tears, so my father asked my mother to take me to Gokomere to inquire on the issue. During our conversation with the headmaster of Gokomere, he told us they would have offered me a place, but Bonda had refused to let me go. A lump clogged my throat. Why was I being forced to return to Bonda when I had made it clear that I wanted to leave? We left Gokomere empty-handed. I felt defeated and hopeless.

My father and I tried a few more times to see if something could be done, but it eventually became apparent that the decision had been made. After days of sulking and crying, my father told me to wipe away my tears and look at it from a positive perspective: I would be returning to my old school with my friends and I would not have to waste any time settling unlike if I had gone to a new school. So, that's exactly what I did! I wiped away my tears and looked forward to seeing my old friends again, determined to succeed in my A-levels like never before.

During those difficult weeks, my father taught me some important lessons. When we work hard but things still don't turn out the way we'd hoped, it's okay to cry and feel disappointed. But, having cried, he also taught me when it is time to let go and how to move on.

In hindsight, I have no regrets about going back to Bonda. I was happy to see my friends again and, even if I had gone to Gokomere, I would have faced the same problem with subject selection; I had no idea which ones to choose. All I knew was that I wanted to be an engineer.

After seeking assistance from the teachers, I was told that mathematics, physics, and chemistry would *probably* be the best options. Unfortunately, there was no career guidance in schools in those days. Neither did tech girls, like me, have any engineers as role models from whom we could get advice. So, with no way of knowing anything different, these are the subjects I selected.

Pleasingly, I was not alone. We were nine girls studying mathematics, physics, and chemistry for A-level; MPC as it was popularly known: the Mad People's Combination. We all worked hard, encouraged one another, and our teachers always went the extra mile to support us.

Engineering Is Not For Girls

As A-level students at Bonda, we were encouraged to engage pupils from other schools in scholarly discussion and knowledge sharing. So, one day, we set out for the nearby St Faith's School for Boys. We loved these school visits because they allowed us to get out of the school fence and enjoy a change of scenery.

We arrived at the school in our "mother van", as we liked to call her. We called her mother because, though old, she was loyal and loving and had ferried many girls to various destinations for sports tournaments, social visits, and even hospital treatments over the years. I remember her huffing and puffing as Brother Peter, our driver, guided her up the steep terrain to our destination. Finally, we could make out the roofs of the first school buildings among the thick canopy. We drove up a long winding driveway and parked under some trees.

One thing that was glaringly obvious on arrival was the absence of someone to welcome us; a sure sign our hosts lacked enthusiasm for our visit. We milled around our van, taking in the scenery and chatting away, occasionally breaking from our conversations to voice our annoyance to our physics teacher over the rudeness being shown to us by these boys. After about fifteen minutes, a boy appeared, at last, and ushered us to a TV room to wait for our hosts. We received no apology and our annoyance was visible in our expressions.

Arrogance personified best describes the thirteen boys who walked into the TV room a full thirty minutes later. The lead boy spoke in a cool, mocking voice.

"We came to see the girls who claim they will be studying engineering at university." We were dumbfounded. We were not expecting such a "greeting". What callousness. What rudeness. I heard the voice of my childhood friend, John, all over again. I had not realised his words about gender roles had stayed with me until this pompous school boy brought it all back. I had a feeling this visit was not going to end well.

Our teacher must have thought this, too, and quickly stepped in to diffuse what he sensed was a potentially explosive situation. He asked the boys to show us around their school. From the way we rose from our seats and paced out of the room, our anger and irritation were clear to everyone.

The boys took us to their physics and chemistry labs, and we spied mixed reactions on their faces as we discussed what each set of students had studied so far. It was clear they admired our level of understanding. Yet, their deeply etched stereotypes prevented them from accepting us as their equals. This is nothing short of tragic, as research has proven that one of the main reasons so few girls take up STEM subjects is not because they are incapable, but because others discourage them, including their own parents and teachers.[12]

As time went by, the boys argued about every concept we discussed in a clear attempt to rile us up or try to outsmart us. Some of their questions we outright ignored because they were not asked out of genuine intrigue but merely to frustrate. And the ones we answered, we did so with voices of rising pitch to match our rising impatience. We grew more displeased with each passing minute. Eventually, our teacher said enough was enough and that it was time to leave.

As we welcomed the sanctuary of our mother van, everyone let out deep breaths of exasperation. I realised that my head and shoulders had started aching from all the tension I had been feeling. Our teacher was the first to speak.

"Well done, girls. I am proud of you," he said, with a huge smile on his face. We smiled back at him and settled into our seats. I became lost in my thoughts about those thirteen rude boys and how I wanted to slap them black and blue. In the picture, I shake them into admitting that boys and girls are academic equals. What a day it had been.

But one thing positive came from that visit. Rather than putting us off studying STEM, as was undoubtedly the aim of those boys, their behaviour sowed a seed in every girl present to show them, and all men like them, how wrong they were. We already knew it was ridiculous that engineering and the sciences should only be considered the domain of men and we returned to school more determined than ever to prove it.

And you know what? We did!

My friends and I continued to study hard at school and revise even harder during the holidays. Eventually, our A-level exams came and went, and when the results came out, I was thrilled. I was going to university! Not only that, but I had obtained the grades I needed to enrol in an engineering course.

"Engineering degree, prepare for me, I am coming for you!" I shouted with joy.

Sadly, the attitude those boys presented is not uncommon. A friend of mine told me once that her father would go into a fit of rage if her brother failed science, yet he did not mind as much if she got low grades in the same subjects. In one school science report, she scored a higher grade than her brother and their father shouted at and chastised her brother for doing worse than her because he was the boy.

By telling boys that they should get better grades in science subjects than their sisters, you are telling them that they are better at science than girls. Not only does this perspective deter daughters from taking science seriously, but the boys will then repeat it to the girls in their class, thereby discouraging them, as well. This denies the world the brilliant minds of countless female scientists. Furthermore, it puts unnecessary pressure on boys to outperform girls in science, when, the truth is, a person's sex has never been a guarantee of being good at any science.

And while the focus of this book is to inspire tech girls who want to study engineering and STEM careers, the problems of entrenched gender stereotypes and gender bias are driving girls and women away from pursuing other careers, as well. Gender inequalities in the US film industry were brought to light in the "Gender Bias Without Borders" study, which demonstrated how gender stereotypes were reinforced by the way females were characterised in movies. The study showed that less than a third of all big-screen speaking roles were played by women.

In fact, the above statistic is relevant to STEM careers. A study by The Lyda Hill Foundation and Mount Saint Mary's University concluded that "Of all STEM characters [portrayed on screen], men outnumbered women nearly two-to-one (62.9% compared to 37.1%)".[13] Thus, how men and women are portrayed in media influences our everyday perceptions of gender roles and, of course, the selection of careers thereafter.

Fortunately, there is hope. There have been several innovative approaches in Africa, applied by both governmental and civil organisations to address the gap concerning women in STEM. Such projects include encouraging women and girls to cultivate a positive attitude towards STEM subjects and careers using models like the one designed by the Forum for African Women Educationalists (FAWE), which has received endorsements and technical support through partnerships with national, regional, and global stakeholders, including ministries of education, corporations, and United Nations agencies. The model has been implemented in thirty-three countries in Africa, including Zimbabwe, through FAWE's national chapters.[14]

So, throughout Zimbabwe, steps are still being taken to increase the number of girls taking up STEM subjects. Still, the uptake remains low. For instance, the proportion of female tertiary graduates in the country in 2013 was just 21.4%.[15] Meanwhile, the proportion of women with jobs in science and engineering fields is less than 28% of the total workforce.[16]

And the problem is arguably even worse worldwide. According to the 2016 Gender Gap Report, women continue to represent the minority of STEM graduates (just 16%).[17] Just like in Zimbabwe, this disparity between men and women is because of the negative stereotypes around women studying STEM subjects and the lack of female role models in STEM fields.

As the figures show, much work remains to be done to close the gender gap in STEM. I have a role to play, you have a role to play, and, together, we can help change attitudes and make it happen.

Summary of Lessons

- It is okay to cry when things don't go the way you expect.
- Do not wallow in failures. Let them go and focus on the positives to move on.
- Career guidance in schools is necessary for children to make informed decisions on the subjects and careers they choose to pursue.
- Media representations of STEM characters impact the acceptance of women in STEM.
- Media role models, parents, educators, and mentors can cultivate girls' interest in maths and science from an early age.
- Early childhood interventions must be implemented to combat stereotypes about science as a pursuit for men only and cultural misconceptions that girls and women have a lower aptitude for STEM.

CHAPTER 8

Surviving University

"No student ever attains very eminent success
by simply doing what is required of him:
it is the amount and excellence of what is
over and above the required that determines
the greatness of ultimate distinction."

—*Charles Kendall Adams*

U niversity life was exciting. You were your own boss: coming from an environment where prefects, matrons, and teachers told you when to do what and how, campus life was liberating. You did what you wanted, when you wanted. If you did not want to attend lectures, no one would make you. If you didn't want to do your assignments, that was your choice. And if you skipped a test, no one batted an eyelid.

Of course, if you didn't do the work, it would all be for naught. Those who were not motivated to learn would fail their classes. The magic word was discipline. You had to manage your time well. Compared to school, university offers freedom in abundance, but many are swallowed up by that freedom.

That was not going to be me! I would not let anything or anyone distract me. I was here for a purpose and that purpose would be fulfilled.

One such distraction I was determined to avoid was boys. Back in high school, my friends and I had heard how common it was for senior boys at university to stampede towards the first-year girls. How they would profess their love until the end of time or how, if the girls should refuse to reciprocate their love, they would surely die. Well, I decided that they'd better get ready to dig some graves if they thought about knocking on my door.

In my first year, I shared a room with a lovely girl called Anna. Anna had a boyfriend from high school who had joined the university with her and was a regular visitor to our room. At least this boy had encouraged Anna to study and they had both made it to university; unlike those boys from St Faith's School that had not one iota of respect for ambitious women.

Unfortunately, this attitude persisted at university. Some boys would brag about how they would never allow their wives or girlfriends to attend university. Or else, they'd laugh that girls could be manipulated because we are "too emotional". I disliked these boys the moment I encountered them. This was pure wickedness. Would they have the pomposity to say such things if the girl in question was their sister? I decided that I had to deal with such men with an iron fist if I was to make it through university, especially as I ended up enrolling on a civil engineering course, where I was one of only two women in a class of twenty men. I was walking into the lion's den, but I would walk out the other side unharmed.

You see, although I knew I wanted to study engineering, I was not familiar with just how many branches of the discipline existed. In my first days on campus, I learnt about electrical engineering, mining engineering, mechanical engineering, civil engineering, agricultural engineering, and metallurgy. My head was swimming by the end of this induction and I wasn't sure which one of the programmes to take. I decided to take a tour of the various departments, seeking clues on what each of these programmes offered. All had their perks, but most didn't inspire me.

Finally, I explored the civil engineering department and I was stunned by the diversity of the models before me: buildings, bridges, water and sanitation infrastructure, and roads. This variety appealed to me because I knew I would always be engaged in whatever roles I took on, as each would be different from the last. It meant I would not be bored doing the same thing all the time. It meant I would have to use my creativity to design and build structures that would each serve a unique purpose. I would be responsible for creating the world around me by designing buildings that would shelter people, bridges to bring them together, and roads to help them move around. My work would change people's lives for the better in innumerable ways. I would be making an impact on the communities around me, just as I had wanted. My heart quickened with excitement and I signed up immediately.

Despite that year's civil engineering intake comprising just one other girl, it just so happened that I knew her. Rose had been a classmate in high school. I had not known she had earned the points she'd needed to enrol, as well, so we hugged and jumped with excitement when we reunited. I later learnt that two other girls from our high school class were studying engineering: one was studying electrical engineering and the other opted for agricultural engineering. Of the nine girls, four made it into engineering that year. The other five girls chased other careers in business and accounting.

So much for girls not being capable of studying at university!

Rose and I supported each other for the next four years, each driving the other to stay focused and work hard. We sat next to each other in lectures, attended the same practical group, studied together, and motivated one another. And my drive to work hard and success was further fuelled by the leadership skills, discipline, and organisation my family had helped me learn from a young age. Engineering was demanding and the days were long: lectures sometimes lasted from eight am until seven pm. And while other students were in town having fun or watching movies on a Friday night, I would be running from lab to lab or studying well into the night for my next test. I wanted this and I was going to get it. I wanted to make my parents and siblings proud.

But despite my steely determination, Rose and I were still the only two girls in a class of twenty boys, so we stood out, especially on a so-called "man's course". Our grades were every other student's business. They had to see how the girls were holding up in this tough degree. I am proud to say we challenged them every step of the way. The boys would never accept being beaten by a woman on any test or exam; yet, it was a bitter pill some of them had to learn to swallow time and again.

In time, the atmosphere became more friendly. The boys in our class kept away from us for the first few weeks. Probably trying to figure out how we were wired and if we were real girls or if we grew horns when it got dark.

It probably didn't help that I had a hat I loved wearing around campus. It was a black cap with the word "BOY" on the front in bold, white letters. Thus, people started to call me Boy when they didn't know my real name. I don't even remember who had bought that cap for me. It added a dash of mystery to who I was and I loved it. But it also meant that some boys were enticed by me. They saw me as something they wanted to capture and possess.

However, once Rose and I showed that we did not bite and that we were their equals intellectually, the boys started to look out for us. Finally, we were one big engineering family. I had proved myself worthy of joining the boy's club and I had the support of my classmates and our lecturers. Rose and I started to feel safe when we were hanging out with them, and we did so at every opportunity.

Yet, while I had earned the respect and trust of my course peers, I still had to confront the other boys on campus. At the faculty, for example, you would sometimes bump into senior boys who had seated themselves in strategic places to ogle the passing girls.

I was losing my patience with these boys and was not prepared to accept their leering gaze. Their pathetic stares were met with a fierce one of my own; one that dared them to speak if they had the guts. I would watch their expressions change to ones of amazement and then unease.

Sadly, this problem was not always confined to campus, either.

I liked to study in my room more than anywhere else. I went to study in the library once and the quietness of the place had made my head ache. One evening, as Anna and I settled down to study, we heard a knock on the door and a tall, lanky, young man entered. I did not recognise him, yet he headed straight for my desk, quickly and decisively. I did not get up but, instead, positioned my chair in such a way that I could look directly at him, fully aware of how unnerving it can be to be stared at right in the eyes.

"Yes?" I responded.

It was clear he had not expected such a bold and direct opening and was thrown off guard immediately. He'd probably revised some speech he'd wanted to recite to me. Instead, he only managed to stammer his name and that he was a third-year engineering student.

"What can I do for you?" I asked with a straight face and a cool voice.

"Well, I was wondering if we could be friends?" he replied.

"No, I have all the friends I need at the moment. If there is nothing else, I would like to continue studying."

There was nothing sensible he could say or do, so he quietly retreated the way he'd come.

And that was how I would proceed to handle every boy who thought he might be able to distract me from university studies. I was never abusive and neither would I shout, I was always polite, and I would simply explain to each one that I did not have time for them. I had been dealing with boys knocking on my door since primary school, but I had made up my mind early on that one must establish themselves in their career of their choice before looking for love. Mama referred to this philosophy as the three Bs: books before boys!

I was not going to change now; now that I was so close to realising my dream of getting an engineering degree.

It's not easy being a woman in an institution of higher learning, which is why it is on you to focus. There will be many people and things clamouring for your attention. Some might seem shiny at first, but be careful they do not rob you of your future. And while friends will give you support and help you relax, you must define your boundaries if you are to meet your goals. If you need to work, don't be afraid to say no to people and try not to fret about whether everyone likes you. It is better to be disliked for the right reasons than to be liked for the wrong ones. You know why you are at university and how much hard work you had to put in to get there, so keep your eyes on the prize.

If you do find yourself in trouble, seek support. Whether you are failing a class, suffering from a break-up, or unexpectedly pregnant, friends and family can be your guiding light. And where they won't help you, look to your professors and supportive organisations, instead. No problem is worth sacrificing your hard work or your life, especially boys. As I like to say, it is your family that will lose someone if you let a relationship destroy you, not the boy's.

Having firmly established my boundaries, I continued my university studies with grit and determination. I enjoyed my time with my friends, but I worked even harder to fulfil my dream. Then, four years later, I passed my final exams and graduation day arrived! The day I had imagined during all those late-night study sessions. The day I had focused on whenever my life was consumed by nothing else but lecture rooms and laboratories. It was finally here. I had made it!

I wore a brown tailor-made suit made just for the event with silk stockings and heeled shoes. After casting away the "boy" cap, I wore my hair in a way few others had ever seen. I knew I looked great and so did Rose.

When our names were called, we walked with our heads held high, the pride shining on our faces as we climbed the podium steps to kneel beside the then President of Zimbabwe. He touched my head with a cushion specifically used to cap graduates, and I rose to my feet a civil engineering graduate.

That day was made all the sweeter by the presence of my parents. They had supported me from the beginning and I saw how proud they were of me. Yes! Thanks to their support, I had realised my dream!

While I worked hard to achieve my degree, I know that I was lucky to receive a government grant to pay my fees. Unfortunately, times and politics change, so it is not as easy to secure funding these days, meaning many students (or their families) have to pay their way through university.

But do not despair! Where students cannot raise the fees, some companies and organisations offer scholarships. They are competitive, but you might be chosen.

And if not, it is common for university students to work jobs during the holidays or even at university. You can even opt to study part-time over a longer period, so you can fit work around your lectures.

Finances are an unfortunate reality of university, but there are plenty of options available. So long as you are determined to achieve your goals, you will find a way!

Summary of Lessons

- There is a time for everything in life. At school and university, you should focus on your studies.
- Suicide is never the answer. Find a person or organisation to give you guidance and support.
- Do not be deterred from your goals or your dreams, even when you are in the minority.
- Hard work always pays off in the end.

The two people who gave me life, Irene and Elisha. I appreciate them for their love and support that made me the woman I am today, December 2019.

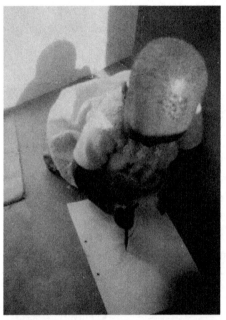

At the age of three, I was holding crayons with much determination. I loved to sit and scribble away.

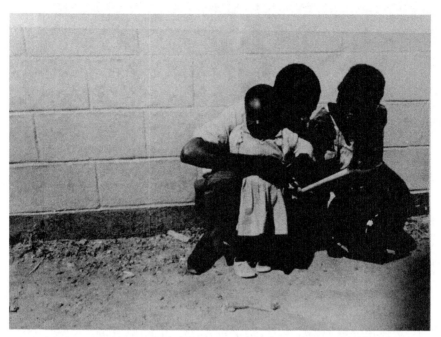

My father and aunt Dorothy liked reading books to me. It seems like I had exhausted my concentration span, but that did not seem to deter them.

Bald or not, I loved my Rose and in my arms is where she belonged. My younger sister sits by my side with her doll.

Christmas day of 1977 in Seke. My siblings and cousins gathered around grandmother at the entrance of her hut. I was sitting on the right next to her, with a yellow party hat.

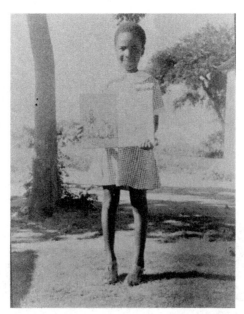

I am proudly showing off my book prize for the best student in my Grade 3 class - Seke, 1982.

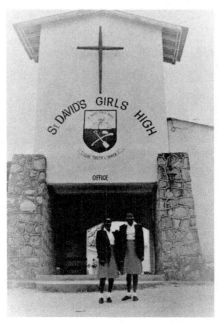

Chiratidzo has been my best friend and sister over the years. Our friendship started in form 1, 1987.

We carried out numerous laboratory experiments during physics lessons. I loved to lead, so I had to be the one pouring the water.

*I was excited because my father had visited me at
school. I could not even look at the camera.*

*The smiles on my mother and father's faces say it all. I won a prize
for obtaining the best IGCSE results in the school (9 A's).*

We had a school trip to the Birchenough bridge in Chimanimani in 1989. Little did I know that I would be back to this same bridge as a university student on attachment later in 1995.

The Golden Stool, a present from my father on my 21st birthday.

Also, a present from my father on my 21st birthday was a Kora guitar.

The big field separated the engineering faculty from the university's administration block. It was a route I took each day to attend lectures - University of Zimbabwe, 1993.

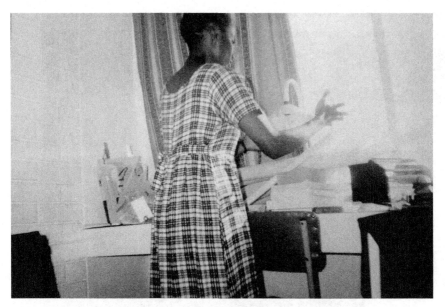

The famous desk in my room at university. Many exams and tests were studied for from here - University of Zimbabwe, 1994.

I was attached to Costain Zimbabwe during the third year of university.

With my usual cheerleaders before we left home for my university graduation.

I was capped by the then President for the Republic of Zimbabwe, the late Comrade Robert Gabriel Mugabe. I was now officially a civil engineering graduate, 1996.

Standing with my mother after the graduation ceremony,
with my degree certificate safely in my hand.

The girls flanking me were from my high school and
had also pursued degrees in engineering.

*In 2013 I graduated from Africa University with a
Master's degree in Business Administration.*

I am inspecting ductile iron pipes laid by a contractor on a project in Uganda, 2017.

During a project hand over exercise in Tanzania, 2019.

All work and no play make the engineer dull. At the Eiffel Tower in France, 2017.

"Catch them young". My daughter, Tanatswa.

I loved that long, thick, black hair. Tanatswa, before we left home for her first day at a new school.

Proud mother and daughter moment. Tanatswa had won a trophy for best sportswoman at an athletics tournament.

We decided to take photos first before we drove to school for a hockey tournament. Tanatswa was later selected to represent the Harare region.

At the age of four, I introduced Tanatswa to the water.

She grew into a force to reckon with in swimming,
representing her school in various galas.

Tanatswa getting a medal for sportswoman of the year - Uganda, 2017

A medal for the Most Valuable Player in basketball, 2018.

*Showing them how it's done at a soccer tournament. Their
school won the trophy for the first position.*

*I took Tanatswa with me to the site during weekends
when she was not going to school.*

Selfie moments on site when everyone else had gone away for the day.

*She is the daughter I want; the reason I get out of
bed every morning, December 2019.*

CHAPTER 9

Lessons From My Mother

"The influence of a mother in the lives
of her children is beyond calculation."

—*James E. Faust*

One reason I have benefited from such supportive and progressive parents is that they also suffered from the consequences of a society that oppresses women.

For as long as I can remember, my mother, Irene Hatikanganwi Garapo, has been a nurse, a job she performs to such a standard as to garner regular praise from her co-workers. So gentle is her touch and so caring her nature that an injection from her is barely noticeable: while other nurses might drive a needle into your flesh and leave behind it a trail of fire, it is but a tiny sting with my mother. And it is a common occurrence for healed patients to return to show their appreciation for her kind and skilled treatment. Perhaps she inherited this gift from her paternal grandmother, who was a well-known traditional herbalist and healer, as well. Whatever the case, I am always filled with pride whenever I see her moving up and down the corridors in her white uniform and brown shoes. For as much as nursing is a nurturing job, I acknowledge that my mother is a scientist in her own right, too.

As I got older, I understood that my mother being a qualified nurse is not something to be taken for granted. Back when she was a child, most fathers did not educate their daughters. They didn't want to spend money only for the daughter then to leave and get married, taking the fruits of that education (knowledge and wealth) to another family. Other more extreme families would even declare that all girls were prostitutes who were certain to drop out of school after getting impregnated, so investing in their education was a worthless act. This made me wonder, how did she get to be a nurse in the face of so much bigotry?

My mother grew up on a farm. Her father was a hard-working farmer and an intelligent man who made a lot of money from farming with the help of my grandmother, an equally hard worker. A significant chunk of the money they earned was put towards the education of their children: five boys and three girls, of whom my mother was the youngest girl.

Because my grandfather had studied agriculture at Nyanyadzi, he valued education and sought to provide one to all his children. Unfortunately, my mother's eldest brother was not very gifted in school. He quit after Grade Four and asked his father not to waste any more money on his education. Another brother was expelled from school after getting involved in a school demonstration and a third dropped out at Grade Five. One of my mother's sisters also dropped out of school after getting pregnant.

Whilst all this was happening, my mother's sister, Madeleine, passed her exams and started her training to become a teacher. It was a great achievement, and she made her parents very proud.

At this time, my mother and her youngest brother, who were now the only remaining children in the family still in school, were due to move into Form Three. As was their family custom, my mother and her brother approached their father at the beginning of a new term to receive the money to fund it. Both waited expectantly as my grandfather opened the tin where he kept the money. He counted out a heap of coins and gave them to my mother's brother, who collected the coins and tied them in a piece of cloth. My mother watched perplexed as her father then closed the tin with a decisive click and asked for it to be returned to his room. She spoke up immediately, asking for her share of the money for her school fees, but he simply replied that he did not have it for her.

His words were like a sword piercing her soul and my mother ran out of the house in tears. She was confused because the tin still had money inside; more than enough to pay for her school fees. What did he mean, he didn't have money for her schooling?

Madeleine came home that weekend on a short break from teacher training college and found my mother crying. Determined that my mother would continue her education, Madeleine paid the fees for the first term herself. She also purchased a new suit, some jerseys, and blankets for her father, as well as new clothes for her mother.

However, it seemed this good fortune would not last. When my mother was about to commence the second term of the year, Madeleine got married. My mother cried her eyes out at the wedding because she knew Madeleine would not be able to pay for her once she left for her new husband's home. She felt doomed.

With school about to resume, my grandfather called my mother into his room. She could hardly believe her ears when he asked her how much were her school fees for the second term and reached for the tin of money. She was overjoyed and thought she might be dreaming, but another part of her wanted to reject the money for how bitter she still felt towards him.

Ultimately, she accepted the money. After all, he was still her father and her future was at stake.

Years went by before she would discover what had happened that strange year. She went on to complete her O-levels and, while she enrolled for teacher's training initially, she later realised that her passion was in nursing. All the while, her father continued to pay her fees.

It was during a break from her nursing training that my mother eavesdropped on her father talking with his friends. He was telling them to never be deceived to not educate girls. After all, it had been his girls who had remembered him and bought him suits, jerseys, blankets, and many other things. His boys, meanwhile, had never even bought him a pair of socks, yet it had been they who had told him, years ago, not to continue to send his youngest daughter to school. He voiced his regret at having listened to them but was happy it had not been too late to remedy the situation.

My mother learnt that what had caused her father to refuse to pay her school fees was her own brothers' jealousy that only the girls in the family seemed to be excelling. Fortunately, my grandfather saw sense and my mother went on to become a successful nurse.

It must have been torture for my mother to not understand why her father had suddenly changed his mind about the importance of her education. But I am proud she voiced her inner warrior to stand up to the cultural barriers in her way. She fought to make sure she got an education and a career.

No two people are alike. Patriarchal societies are quick to label women as unworthy of education or less important than the men of the family. And yet, my mother's story shows sometimes it is the women who are the better academics and the more successful professionals.

We must do better at equipping all our children with the necessary skills to make it through life. No child is more important than another. They all have unique skills that will contribute to the family's livelihood and the country's prosperity at large. The fact that one happens to be a girl does not mean they are incapable of contributing anything towards the family's livelihood. Just look at how my aunt Madeleine rewarded my grandparents for their support with gifts.

Alas, many families still treat girls unfairly by not giving them the same level of support in their academic or career endeavours that they do for boys. Sometimes this comes in the form of financial support, like what happened to my mother. Other times, it comes in the form of gender role bias. For instance, boys are encouraged to take up more activities and sports and they often have more time to study at home because they are not expected to do so many chores around the house. Because girls are expected to do more housework, they have less time for sports, hobbies, and study. Not only does this tell boys and girls that they are different, but also it denies girls the same amount of time to develop their academic skills or the confidence and leadership traits that come from sports and club activities.

Parents, you know your daughter is capable of anything. Give her the same opportunities as you do your other children and she will thrive!

Summary of Lessons

- You must fight for what you want.
- It is never too late to retrace your steps and make things right.
- Support boys and girls equally in their endeavours.
- For a family or society to be wholly inclusive, we must incorporate the voices of women.

CHAPTER 10

Conversations With My Father

"My DAD has given me the best GIFT
anyone has ever given me.
He gave me wings to fly."

—*Adria Arjona*

E very son and daughter's first sense of what it means to be a man comes from their father. They are the ultimate role models when it comes to defining how men should treat women. My father is the first man in my life. To me, he represents everything a man should be.

My father, Elisha Tofireyi Chitehwe Makumbe, grew up in a polygamous family, which was not so unusual back then. His father's first wife had eight children, the second (my father's mother) had four children, and the last had three children.

It is hardly surprising my grandfather married three women as he had been a charming man who was very quick-witted. My father inherited his charm and humour, and I believe I inherited them from my father.

In a polygamous family, each wife is in charge of their own home and children, while the husband moves from one home to the next. In addition to caring for his wives and children, my grandfather farmed his fields to support the three households.

Naturally, the children helped with the chores. So, my father learnt teamwork and hard work when he helped in the fields, sometimes waking up at five am to work before going to school. And he learnt independence and responsibility when he carried out chores at home, often without any adult supervision.

The number of chores that needed doing meant my father never experienced gender bias in his family, besides the one husband, three wives dynamic. Boys and girls were expected to work equally hard, taking it turns to plough the fields, fetch firewood, and cook the family meals. As a result, he developed an attitude that the two sexes are equally capable in their endeavours and became more persuaded still by this argument when he later studied child psychology. Furthermore, as a teacher, he would frequently observe girls outperforming boys in science classes. Naturally, then, my father supported every child in our family equally, regardless of gender. There were school fees for all and he would always take the time to encourage each of my siblings and me according to our strengths and weaknesses.

One of the consequences of being a polygamous husband who moves from home to home is you don't ever really belong in any of them. My grandfather became a neglected man because each wife presumed the next would look after him. At the end of the day, each wife was busy looking after their own home and children that they could not be available to care for him or even to prepare him some food.

My father, a young boy then, became his father's keeper. He made sure his father had food to eat and he was there to help him with any additional chores. Often, this meant my father would be slower to complete his own chores and some family members would reprimand him for it. Yet, this did not deter my father, who remained defiant in helping my ageing grandfather.

Past societies have glorified polygamy as a sign of manhood but my grandfather found himself alone and miserable. Without the support of his many wives, the old man found a true son in my father. I want to believe it is this seed sown in my father at such a tender age, to look out for the underdog, which led him to develop a need to look out for his daughters and teach them to stand up for themselves, as he knew that society would try to oppress them. I have mentioned how he would help me to study the subjects I struggled with in new ways to find the approach that worked best for me, but his lessons extended to life as a whole, too.

For example, after failing to reverse through the drums a couple of times as I prepared for my driver's test, he showed me how to do it using a toy car on our dining table. The next time I went for a driving test, I brought home my licence. He always made it clear he would support me as I found my way in life, which gave me confidence whenever I tackled new challenges. If ever I failed something, he would ask me, "Did you try your best?" If my answer was yes, then he would say, in a calm, reassuring voice, "So, don't cry. You did your best and that is all that matters. You will have better luck next time." If my answer was no, he would ask why and work with me to see my shortcomings and help me improve.

A father who supports and helps their children gives them confidence and, with confidence, you can accomplish anything. I had tonnes of it and it set me apart as a winner. My confidence is how I carried myself through school and university. I would answer anyone that asked me if sciences were the course for me with a strong yes. Yes, I could do it. And I believed it because my father believed in me.

As parents, you have the power to instil confidence in your children. The more they believe you love them, want what's best for them, and will help them achieve their goals and improve themselves, the more they will believe in themselves. It begins with you and it must start now.

And fathers who want their daughters to reach their potential must give them the confidence that they can succeed in whatever path they choose. Even careers often ascribed to men, like STEM. Daughters look to their fathers to learn how women can expect to be treated by men. Teach them that they are worth the highest levels of respect, that they are equal with men, and they will believe it and go out into the world to prove it.

My father grew up a hard worker, so he trained me to work hard, as well. I was taught nothing good ever comes easily. He imprinted in my mind the image of a responsible man as one that took care of his family and valued education, and I never missed a day of school because of the non-payment of school fees. A man for me became someone of a sober mind. Not once in my life did I see my father raise a hand to strike my mother. Women were to be respected at all times.

As a father, are you willing to take the time to be a part of your daughter's life? Celebrating with her in her successes and crying with her during her struggles? To give her guidance on how to manoeuvre the stormy seas we must sometimes face in this world? Fathers, your daughters need you. Take their hand and guide them. Sit them down for a chat because every daughter values her conversations with her father. Be patient, kind, and humble. Above all, show them that a *real* man is one who values and respects women as their equal.

Summary of Lessons

- Nothing good comes easily.
- A father's presence and duty in his daughter's life gives her an appreciation of what to expect from the other men in her life.

CHAPTER 11

The Princess In Me

"I want to be respected in all of my
femaleness because I deserve to be."

—*Chimamanda Ngozi Adichie*

For my twenty-first birthday, I visited my parents in Ghana, where my father had been posted for four years. All my siblings were present and clamouring to contribute in some way to my milestone event. This was a nice change as it was always such a mammoth task to get my siblings to do anything around the house under normal circumstances. My mother and I went to the market to buy the ingredients she needed to prepare the new spicy dishes she had learnt to cook. The house was full of love and energy and I remember trying on various clothes to make sure I looked my best.

On the day of the celebrations, everyone looked beautiful, including my mother and father, who wore their new Ghanaian outfits. After a delicious lunch, we all retreated to the sitting room for presents and speeches. My mother gave me some gold earrings whilst my siblings gave me a wallet, a homemade card, and tee-shirts. I loved all my presents.

Then, my father approached me with his presents. He was grinning as he handed them over to me. Both were wrapped in shiny gold paper. The attention that my father had afforded them made me nervous with anticipation and my siblings gathered close to see them. I unwrapped them to reveal a Ghanaian golden stool and a kora guitar. I am someone who loves cultural artefacts, so these two gifts blew me away. But it was my father's narration of their significance that truly made them worthwhile.

The golden stool is the royal and divine throne of kings of the Ashanti tribe. Such seats were symbolic of the chieftain's leadership. Meanwhile, the kora guitar is a stringed instrument made from a calabash and covered in cow skin. These guitars have been in use for over five thousand years and were usually strummed while accompanying storytelling performances, songs, and poetry recitals, the latter of which I could relate to because I had written poetry in school, some of which had been published in magazines.

With the stool, I felt that my father had acknowledged my leadership as the firstborn. And with the guitar, he gave encouraged me to rediscover my love of poetry with the hope of one day performing it.

As you can imagine, I was blown away by these gifts and they have had a profound effect on my ever since. Quite simply, I consider myself royalty. My parents treated me with the respect and expectation of a princess of the Chiweshe clan. Like a princess, I was born a leader and raised with this notion deeply ingrained in me.

The gifts simply formalised what I already knew to be true.

It is a Shona belief that anyone who is royalty is welcomed with showers of rain when they visit a new place or somewhere they have not visited in a long time. This is true of me. The rain has showered every time I have visited anywhere new. A place that is parched before my arrival will suddenly experience showers of rain and people have joyfully told me that I had brought it with me. Call it coincidence or whatever you like, I know I am royalty. Why? Because I expect nothing less than to be treated like the princess that I am; and this is true for all of us tech girls! A princess is someone that deserves the best in life. She is someone who will not tolerate any voice that says she is anything other than complete or special. A princess says, "I can" and "I will". My voice matters and I will not tolerate any disrespect.

My twenty-first was not just a birthday milestone. By truly believing I am a princess and deserving of respect, I am able to appreciate my achievements and the people in my life so much more.

There have been times when I have had to work two or three jobs to ensure I had a good place to sleep and food on the table. When competition for jobs on the market was stiff and people with master's degrees were being given preference over those with honour's degrees, I went out and got myself a master's degree. When I was told that, to get a managerial position, one had to have a Master's in Business Administration (MBA), I went and got one. I had to have the best out of life. I allowed no one to disrespect me at the workplace and I would speak my mind because no one would disrespect the princess in me. Years later, when I had my daughter, I would only consider the best schools for her because only the best was good enough for my own princess. Like me, I wanted her to experience the best of what this life has to offer.

Giving presents may seem like a small act to some, but they are often large ones to our children and leave long-lasting impressions. If they feel they matter and are cared for at home, they will never accept anyone treating them any less in the rest of the world. They will stand tall and proud knowing that they are someone who matters and must not tolerate any disrespect. So, show your children that they matter at every opportunity.

Summary of Lessons

- The small acts of love and care we give our children impact their lives in a big way.

CHAPTER 12

A Woman Alone In A Male-Dominated Arena

"The male-dominated systems know they
cannot maintain their current power structures
if and when the woman is restored to her natural
and powerful state as a great leader and co-creator."

—Bryant McGill

On most construction sites, it is unlikely you will find many (or any) technical working women. While this is starting to change (very slowly), men have become used to working on these sites without women and they have become quite protective of their territory. Many, then, can be quite resistant to a woman on site, which they often voice via sexist utterances, like, "do you think you will become a man by hanging out with the boys?" or "why don't you find another job with more of your kind, so that you do not feel out of place?"

"Well," I reply, "I do not want to be a man. I am a full woman and I love being a woman. I just so happen to love engineering, too. And while we might be different genders, I would like to think that our passion for engineering is something that bonds us in a way far stronger than our gender differences divide us."

Unfortunately, this doesn't always serve and just the sight of a woman on site can be enough to offend. I have even been asked to dress like a man if I want contractors to take my instructions seriously. Again, I deny them because I am not in the business of pretending to be a male engineer. I am a female engineer! I dress to my taste, in a manner that is practical and professional for working on site. The contractor would take my instructions seriously based on my knowledge of the works. Likewise, I won't imitate a man's voice to bark out commands to be taken seriously. I will use my own voice, in my own way, and be taken seriously out of respect for my knowledge and skill.

Tech girls, it is important to define how you want to behave at work and then stick to your guns to ensure people respect you. This is especially true when entering a work arena traditionally dominated by men. If they try to encourage or force you to change, refuse! If they disrespect you, show them up as fools. Be respectful and professional where possible, but always stand your ground.

Here are some of my own stories of confrontation with sexism in the workplace and how I handled them. I hope they inspire you as you confront your own challenges.

Unwanted Advances

Before I graduated from university, I applied to work with a government organisation to conduct a study of Birchenough Bridge in the Eastern Highlands of Zimbabwe. The bridge is an important link between Chipinge and Buhera, and it needed to be assessed for repairs and maintenance. It would be a great opportunity to put my knowledge into practice, so I was thrilled when they accepted my application.

The bridge is about two-hundred-and-sixty kilometres from Harare, so a senior engineer from the organisation picked me up in a single cabin truck for our two-night trip. I was not familiar with him, but I had bumped into him once or twice in the corridors at work.

Initially, the journey passed in silence. Gradually, the engineer started to ask me questions about my aspirations and ambitions for the future. By the time we had stopped for some food and resumed our trip, he was much more animated and jovial in his stories. He would give me a random punch on the shoulder as he laughed at his own jokes. I sat still and chipped into the conversation where necessary, although I would have preferred to just gaze at the beautiful scenery. In one instance, the engineer's hand grazed my thigh. I took this to be a slip and ignored it. But when it happened a second time, the hand lingered a little longer and I knew this was no mistake.

I contorted my face in anger. What was he up to? What did he take me for? Have I done something to suggest I am interested in him? But this man was my supervisor; what do I do? All these questions were churning around in my head when he gripped my thigh!

That was it. I grabbed his hand and pushed it away forcefully, my fingers shaking with rage. I did not make eye contact with him but, instead, continued looking out of the window, praying he had got the message and would stop groping my legs. Thankfully, he did stop and concentrated on the road. All of a sudden, the beautiful scenery was replaced with a blurry grey screen and we completed the remainder of the long journey in utter silence.

We checked into the best lodge in the area. In some other lodges we had passed, the toilets did not flush, the doors did not lock, or the rooms were filthy. Fortunately, the room I got in the lodge we settled on was decent and I decided to have my supper in there. I was going through my notes in preparation for the following day's site visit when I heard a faint knock on my door.

"It's...it's me," the engineer stammered on the other side of the door. I took a deep breath to steady myself and opened a small crack, just enough to peep outside, my leg wedged against the door.

"Yes?" I asked.

"Have you eaten already?"

"Yes, I have," I said, in a cool, flat voice.

"Oh, okay. I am off to eat, as well."

"Alright. Thank you for checking up on me," I responded as I shut the door.

About two hours later, I had brushed my teeth, put on my night-clothes, and was reading in bed when I heard another soft knock. I knew who it was and I reassured myself that this was a busy lodge, so the engineer wouldn't try anything funny.

"Eh, sorry to disturb you, I see you are already prepared for bed."

"Yes. Is there a problem?"

"Um, do you have toothpaste? My wife forgot to pack some for me."

What a line, right? If I had not been feeling annoyed, I would have burst out laughing. Instead, I said nothing. I secured the door, retrieved some toothpaste from the bathroom, and returned to hand it to him.

"It's alright, you can use it and I will collect it in the morning," I said, dismissively.

"Okay, then. Thanks and good night."

"Good night."

At last, he left and I could relax, secure in myself that I had stood up to a difficult situation while remaining professional and courteous.

Some years later, I encountered a more extreme situation while working for a local authority. I was the head of the engineering department and my boss had taken a fancy to me. This was a man who was old enough to be my father and had children who were my age. Sure, age is nothing but a number, but I made it crystal clear to him on numerous occasions that I wasn't interested. Unfortunately, he would not take no for an answer. He even invited some of his friends to come to his office to try and convince me to begin a relationship with him. Thereafter, I dreaded being summoned to his office, never sure if it was for some genuine work reason or something more sinister.

The harassment would continue in other ways, as well. I started taking another route home after work when I found out my boss would stand by the window overlooking the road to watch me. This was quickly getting out of hand. To make matters worse, the other heads of department eventually got wind of what was going on, but rather than supporting me, they would cast lewd eyes in my direction during meetings. My continued refusal of these advances led to authority suspending me. Officially, I was accused of incompetence and blamed for the lack of refuse collection.

For seven months, I received no salary and sat at home with nothing to do. I contemplated resigning and finding another job elsewhere. But I changed my attitude after a conversation with my mother. After I updated her on my suspension and the course of action I had resolved to take, she looked me straight in the eyes and said, "You have decided to quit? To run away? If you run, what about the other girls who are being harassed by this same man. What chance do they have?"

That was all I needed to become a woman on a mission. I would fight this sexual harassment and win. My mother was right, I was no quitter. I was stronger than that. I would not to be taken for granted or tolerate such behaviour.

Right away, I engaged a lawyer to talk to my employer to set a date for a hearing to contest the allegations being levelled against me. Together, we collected proof that there had been no refuse collection because the council had no diesel for the trucks and the department responsible for the fuel purchases had repeatedly stated that they did not have the money to buy the fuel. I had even highlighted this issue in departmental meetings.

A month passed and I heard nothing from the lawyer. It seemed all he would do was call me to ask for more money to make one high court application after another. I later learnt that he was a friend with the big bosses in the council. I felt cheated. Was that what the judicial system had become? Where could the victims like me seek recourse?

While pondering what to do next, I remembered meeting a female member of parliament who had visited our town and given me her business card. I went to see her and told her my story. She advised me to take my issue to the Ministry of Local Government and National Housing while she engaged with others she felt could assist me. I felt scared. I had never met a minister face-to-face before. But I would not back down now. I was determined to see this through.

After meeting with the minister and relaying my plight, he was appalled. He immediately called someone into his office and instructed them to handle my case and ensure I got back to work. I was told to go home and that someone would be in touch. I returned home a happier woman and felt relieved the wheels had begun to turn. There was hope, at last.

A swift and devastating avalanche followed. A government directive was issued to the council for my reinstatement with immediate effect, including backdated payment of my salary and benefits to the date of my suspension. Even better, my old boss was gone upon my return and I never saw him again.

The victory was sweet. I felt like a warrior princess returning from battle as I resumed work. Everyone congratulated me for being strong and standing firm, and I was surprised to learn my story had spread through the department like a veldt fire. Some girls approached me privately and told me they had been harassed by the same man, but they had not reported it for fear of being victimised and dismissed from their jobs. They applauded me for having brought the insanity to an end.

As for my mother, she smiled when I updated her on the issue and I knew she was proud of me.

By the way, you might be interested in knowing what I did with the bag of money I got from my backdated pay and benefits. Well, I bought my first house!

I know that I am not alone when it comes to experiencing sexual harassment in the workplace. Plenty of female engineers have left good roles and settled for work in environments they consider "friendlier" to women .

Many women consider construction sites and offices no-go zones because they fear being sexually harassed.

And this problem is not limited to STEM careers. A survey by the Ministry of Women's Affairs, Gender and Community Development carried out in Mutare, Zimbabwe, revealed that 85% of female workers are being sexually harassed at their respective workplaces.[18]

Nor is the issue of sexual harassment isolated to Zimbabwe. The International Labour Organisation concluded that nearly a quarter of workers surveyed in Hong Kong have suffered harassment of a sexual nature (and one-third of that number was men).[19] A report in Italy published that over half of the surveyed women aged fourteen to fifty-nine have been victims of sexual harassment, one in three women are subjected to sexual intimidation (65% of whom are blackmailed by their harasser), and the majority of victims end up resigning from their job. These figures are comparable to those throughout the European Union. And according to a survey by the Australian Equal Opportunity Commission, almost one in five interviewees between the ages of eighteen and sixty-four said they had been the victims of sexual harassment at work, yet only a little more than a third said they would report the incidents.[20]

As the statistics above show, men are sexually harassed in the workplace, as well. However, they are less likely to speak up because they fear they will be ridiculed. This is one of the terrible consequences of raising boys to feel they must be strong all the time and not share their emotions. Just as society needs to condemn sexual harassment and women should be protected when they report it, male victims should not be mocked, but praised for their bravery at coming forward.

Tech girls, when you work in a predominantly male environment, you have to be tough. You must define your boundaries on what is acceptable and what is not. Do not feel intimated, even if the harasser is someone in a senior position. A no is a no, and you must report any cases of sexual harassment to save yourself and the next would-be victim from the culprits. Yes, it is likely the harasser and even the employer will try to intimidate you into staying quiet, perhaps by threatening to take your job away from you. But you can protect yourself and your co-workers, bring the perpetrators to justice, and make the environment a better place to work by standing up to sexual harassment.

The Dreaded Fight

When I was twenty-eight and employed by a local authority as one of their junior water and sanitation engineers, an elderly gentleman approached our offices to have a water meter connected at his plot. I sat the elderly gentleman down and started taking him through what was required from him before we could carry out the work. At some point during this conversation, he decided that he didn't like what I was telling him. I explained that I was simply outlining the rules and regulations as defined by the council. Again, he didn't like this.

"What do you know? You are a mere secretary!" the elderly man spat at me.

At that moment, I saw red. I was a junior engineer, qualified with honours from the University of Zimbabwe! How dare he say such a thing! I began insulting him back. Before I knew it, we were in a shouting match and neither of us was backing down.

There was pandemonium in the corridors as my colleagues, including my boss, rushed to my office. They were greeted by the sight of a young woman and an elderly gentleman jabbing fingers into each other's faces. I was literally shaking like a reed in a river. My boss tried to soothe me, speaking in quiet tones, but I refused to acknowledge him. I had to deal with this foul-mouthed man first. I was tired of such men thinking all women in offices were secretaries, so I continued to rant and rave. The commotion lasted for at least five minutes before I finally allowed my boss to pull me into his office.

As I recall that event now, I laugh at the ridiculousness of the whole picture. But back in my days as a younger engineer, I was determined to give blow for blow. You punch me; I punch you right back. I was full of adrenaline. I was ready for anyone that dared cross my path.

Of course, this didn't help my career at times. My lack of emotional intelligence cost me promotions and, in some instances, my contracts were not renewed. Employers and clients were only too happy to see the back of me sometimes because I couldn't control my temper.

Now, I know better. Tech girls must be emotionally intelligent in their social and professional lives. Sometimes we must manage our emotional response, even in the face of an insult or someone being rude, for a more positive outcome. It's the easiest thing in the world to get angry or fire an insult at a nasty person. But controlling your rage and giving a more measured, intelligent response that benefits you in the long term requires patience, composure, and strength.

France

I am fortunate that I have had opportunities to travel during the execution of some of my projects, including to inspect project equipment and ensure its conformity with regulations and specifications before its shipment. On my first trip to France, my colleague and I visited a factory to inspect how the pumps we'd ordered were being manufactured. Our guide even showed us quality assurance reports to ensure us the pumps would comply with our standards. It was a great tour, the factory was well-equipped, and we had no doubt we would receive a quality product from them.

The following day, my colleague and I met again with the manufacturers to discuss logistics, including shipment timelines. I remember being the only woman at that table, although I was used to this now, so it didn't faze me. I settled in my chair and prepared myself for the discussion to begin, but when the meeting kicked off, I realised that everyone was speaking in French. My male colleague knew perfectly well I did not speak the language, yet he did nothing to remedy the situation. Well, I guess it was up to me, instead.

Back in my days as a young engineer, I would have come close to jumping on top of that boardroom table to loudly and aggressively share my thoughts, but not anymore, tempting though it was. The seasoned engineer in me did nothing of the sort. Instead, I took two deep breaths to calm myself and then interjected.

"Excuse me, I did not come all the way from Africa to look pretty in your boardroom. Can we use English, please?" I said with a sweet-yet-mocking voice. There was a moment of silence in the room as each person took in what I had said and, then, they all started grinning. Moments later, the meeting resumed, this time in English.

I remember replaying the moment later that same day in my hotel room. I looked at myself in the mirror, smiled, and said, "Yes, Joy, way to go, girl! You handled that just like the boss you are!"

Have you ever been physically present in a place but totally ignored? When you could very well be a pot plant or a painting hanging on the wall for all the attention people are giving you? Have you ever felt useless or out of your depth in a situation because no one briefed or consulted you beforehand? What did you do? Did you stay quiet or speak out and, if so, what did you say?

Of course, it's alright to stay silent sometimes. But remember, if you don't speak up, nothing is going to change. It is always up to *you* to show others how you should be treated.

It helps that I am a confident person and I understand not everyone believes they have what it takes to speak up in certain situations. But confidence is a skill and, like any skill, it can be learnt and developed with practice. So, if confidence doesn't come naturally to you, you can start to build it by avoiding the negative people in your life (like those who put you down) and surrounding yourself with those who pick you up. Work on feeling positive about yourself and your achievements. Change your body language (shoulders back, chin up, and look people in the eyes) and dress for success. Over time, you will feel more confident and it will be easier to stand up for yourself.

Work ~~Unappreciated~~

I love to work on a site: being outdoors in the fresh breeze, breathing in the scent of freshly excavated earth or mixed concrete. However, every so often, this is disturbed by the arrival of an important person whom I need to impress.

I remember one such occasion we got wind that the boss of our client's team would be visiting our site. He was passing through the town and had decided to check on our progress. I admit that I felt the tension and expectation as much as anyone else there that day.

Sure enough, an entourage of cars arrived and the man himself jumped out of his car, dressed in an immaculate navy suit and tie. The contractor hurriedly stepped forward to distribute helmets and reflectors to our visitors but it was my duty as the engineer to welcome the visitors, guide them around the site, and answer any questions. So, I moved forward to greet him with my hand outstretched. He took my hand, limply and briefly, whilst shouting for whoever was in charge. I informed him that I was the resident engineer. It seems he didn't believe me because he sought to test me by asking me about a chemical process for treating water at the plant.

Whilst in mid-sentence, he interrupted my response and said to me, "Do you even know what you are doing here?"

That remark hit me like a big cold hand slapping me across the face. What was his problem with me? I felt angry. Do I know what I am doing? What a joke.

I could not let that jibe pass unanswered, but I also knew I needed to stay calm and professional. So, I responded in a cool voice that I knew exactly what I was doing before moving away from him. I would not be drawn into a war of words; it was neither the time nor the place. Besides, it would have been a waste of time as he did not even give me the respect of acknowledging my response. Rather, the best way to deal with such people is to respond with assertiveness and respect and say no more. There's no point in being rude as it will get you in hot water. By this point in my career, I had learnt that one must choose their battles. In this case, his remark did not change the fact that I was the project supervisor, and any insults from me would have only harmed my position. Everyone else from the client's side was commending me on my work and my bosses were happy with my performance. That was what mattered most to me.

Unprepared to deal with his rude attitude, I allowed the contractor to manage the rest of the visit. The client boss would ask his questions, although he didn't get all his answers.

I later learnt that this was simply the guy's character. Everywhere he went, he would belittle the personnel he found on site and no one was expected to complain in return. In fact, if he shook your hand at all, you were lucky. So, I guess I had been lucky, then?

Anyway, I decided not to let his behaviour bother me and my calm reaction earned the respect of my colleagues. It even became an on-site joke where the boys would ask me if I knew what I was doing before we all doubled up with laughter.

When the project was nearly complete, the same guy visited the site for the second time. The boys told me I had to lead, but I refused. I decided to watch the whole scene from a distance. I was interested to see how the day's events would unfold.

However, it wasn't long before I heard him say, "Madame, please tell us what has been going on here." Sure enough, he was looking in my direction and it was clear he was acknowledging me as the person in charge, at last.

I took him through the site activities, highlighting any challenges and our anticipated timeline. He thanked me for a job well done and for sticking with the project from its inception. I could hardly believe my ears. Praise! From this guy! For me!

This taught me something very important: no good thing will ever be ignored. It will stare everyone in the face until it is acknowledged. So, hold on; if you do good work, the praise *will* come. And when others don't praise you enough, make sure to blow your own horn, celebrate your success, and keep doing what you are already doing so well.

I have had to face these professional battles because the patriarchal nature of society assumed I was less competent than my male counterparts. I have been perceived as a problem because I am a strong and intelligent woman. The patriarchy justifies the denial of opportunity for women and feeds the message that men should wield power while women occupy subordinate positions throughout society. One of the ways we can all bring down the patriarchy is to question the conventional gender paradigms and hold everyone to account for their actions and how they treat others. And we do this by empowering women and educating boys and girls to see each other as equals and treat one another with respect. In the words of Eileen Hunt Botting, "The educated woman, with power over herself, can bring down the patriarchy for the betterment of all humanity."

Are you willing to be a part of the movement?

Summary of Lessons

- Define your own boundaries and be firm and consistent about sticking to them.
- All cases of sexual harassment in the workplace must be reported. It will be better for everyone in the long-term and you will create a workplace environment that does not tolerate such behaviour.
- Learn to manage your emotions and responses to enjoy greater success in your personal and professional lives.
- How people treat you will not change if you do not speak up in the situations when you feel you are being marginalised or oppressed.
- Show others how you expect to be treated.
- No good thing can be ignored. Keep doing what you do and the praise will follow.
- There's nothing wrong with celebrating your own successes.

CHAPTER 13

A Tech Heartbeat

"If you find something you feel passionately about,
pursue it with all your heart, and don't let
ANYONE tell you that you're too young
or inexperienced to make it happen."

—*Lauren Kulokas*

To succeed as a tech girl and to change the hearts and minds of those who think you are pursuing the wrong career, you need to be confident about what you do and do it well.

I usually kick start my day with a tour of the site, so I am aware of what we have achieved and what needs to happen next. Sometimes, I tour alone, but it's better if I can walk around with the contractor. Then, I can discuss any challenges and seek solutions as a team.

Despite this habit, no working day is ever the same for me. Some days are more hectic than others and each one has its joys and challenges. But I am almost always satisfied with my contributions, so I have learnt to keep my cool and approach every problem with a level head. I never let others push into making hurried or uninformed decisions, especially as a wrong decision can be costly. This is particularly true of novel or unfamiliar issues, when I like to consult my peers. I believe that nobody should re-invent the wheel; if a challenge needs addressing on my construction site, then it has surely been tackled on other sites before. So, all the advice I need is a mere phone call or email away.

As a woman, I am a minority on site, although I have no problems leading everyone. After all, it is my job as a project manager to motivate the project teams (the contractor and client) to achieve our common goals. So, I make up for people's presumptions of me by making sure my voice is loud and confident on site, so everyone understands what I want to be done (or, in some rare instances, undone). This requires me knowing my stuff, so that, when I speak and manage, I have the trust of those around me, who will then be more likely to accept my leadership.

Usually, the manager determines how well the team works, so I am proud that I have inspired great teams. One way I do this is to make sure to involve the team in the site decision-making activities, so they feel invested and understand the big picture. Of course, the final decisions always lie with me, but by giving everyone a chance to give their input, teams gel together faster and everyone feels more accountable for the work.

Giving teams responsibility is important, even when my instincts tell me to take people by the hand. While I am the leader, I am not anyone's "mum" at work. So, I do not bat an eye when the boys swear at each other, the machines, or their work. Thus, they are more relaxed around me be-cause I do not police their behaviour. If someone decides to eat unhealthy lunches, I might mention, in passing, how they could eat a more balanced diet, but I won't bring anyone a home-cooked meal. Whatever your in-stincts, let them be! They are grown men; they can and should make their own decisions. By knowing where your responsibilities as an engineer be-gin and end on the site, you will be more quickly embraced by the workers.

Of course, as women, we will always be treated a little differently. One aspect I have found fascinating about some of the men I have worked with on sites is when they attempt to act like gentlemen in my presence. In some ridiculous instances, a man has wanted to hold my hand as I balance on a reservoir top slab. Of course, I refute the help. And many have attempted to bring me gifts, including chocolates, special teas, and perfume. Sometimes, I accept the gifts with grace and appreciation, but I am careful to set boundaries, making it clear that I will not grant any favours or allow people to slack off.

Managing these various work teams, as well as the unique challenges I face as a tech girl, requires that I am confident and inspire confidence in the people with whom I work. For me, I have found that dressing professionally and comfortably helps. I know the exact clothes that give me confidence, whether they are jeans or cargo pants, a loose-fitting shirt or a t-shirt, and a hat (if I'm not required to wear a safety helmet) to ward off the scorching sun; I dislike being squeezed and hot as I go about my duties and few things are more uncomfortable on site than feeling like your trousers are too tight and about to rip with every step. Create your own style: find whatever works for you and gives you confidence. Be safe and don't underestimate comfort, but also, dress like the boss you are and your self-esteem will grow.

My confidence is also boosted by knowing the limits of my responsibilities on site. When you have no idea what you are expected to do, your confidence evaporates like morning dew under the rising sun. The contractor is also quick to detect your uncertainty and they will bulldoze you into making decisions that may make their life easier, but your job harder. Ultimately, you will start to resent coming to work. So, take the time to understand the limits of your power on site and, if you feel there are gaps in your knowledge, prepare yourself to study or train.

Still, errors are inevitable and I don't pretend otherwise. I believe that mistakes are for the living, so I am unafraid to make them. Dive into your work and swim like crazy, so you learn as much as possible, as quickly as possible. And always solicit feedback from people who you trust to give you an honest opinion. When I was still green in project management, I worked with Max, a member of the client's project team, who taught me a lot of useful advice. For example, I remember writing a letter to the contractor about getting insurance for the project vehicles. In my letter, I wrote, "please make sure you buy insurance because the vehicles cannot be driven without it". When I asked for feedback from Max, his answer was both a wake-up call and humorous: "Joy, why are you begging the contractor to perform their contractual duties? This 'please' business must stop. Instruct them!"

Another way to earn the respect of your colleagues and teams is to always be on time, be it for a meeting or a site inspection. A person who shows respect for their peers by arriving somewhere when they say will see this respect reciprocated. So, be organised and stay on top of your time management.

As engineers, it is vital we determine the types of contractors working with us. Some are better than others at their various duties and you might need to assist them from time to time. But be careful not to hurt their pride or remove them from the decision-making process. Where a situation arises on site and you have to brainstorm with the contractor for solutions, offer your suggestions but make it clear your ideas are just that and not instructions. The contractor must not be relieved of their obligations. Otherwise, they will either blame you if something goes wrong or feel demotivated because they believe they cannot make their own choices.

Furthermore, try to avoid conflict as much as possible. Always remember that all teams are working to achieve the same goal, even if they forget it sometimes. There is rarely a reason to fight. You all want the same thing at the end of the day. Help conflicting teams to see the shared goal and to find ways to work together peacefully.

Lead your projects with confidence and determination and you may see the benefits impact other areas of your life, as well. For instance, I never realised until late on that my siblings had been watching my professional journey with more interest than I had assumed. Like many of my friends growing up, some of my siblings had not been sure that women could become engineers. But I had become a role model for them. I had broken the societal mould and proven we could all achieve our dreams. My younger sister is now an aircraft engineer, and I am very proud of her.

Moreover, I am influencing the next generation, too. My daughter knows that women can be engineers and I take her with me to site at every opportunity. She has seen me climb ladders and jump between trenches. She has come to appreciate that anything is possible with hard work. Now, she appreciates women can be strong and in control, and that there is nothing wrong with that!

Of course, the better I do my job and the more I inspire my family, the more my other relatives and my community have come to accept that women can be engineers. They used to discourage me but now they feel pride for my accomplishments. I have busted the myths and corrected their beliefs. I always beam with pride at the whispers at our family gatherings: "That is Elisha's daughter, the engineer." And likewise, my face lights up when a mother in our neighbourhood introduces me to her friends as the Makumbe daughter who is intelligent and strong and has ventured into the man's profession of engineering. Eyes round with awe and admiration turn to stare at me. I always use the opportunity to tell them that engineering is no longer a man's profession!

And now I am taking this message to new communities, not just via this book, but also the Joy Makumbe Trust. Girls ask me to visit their youth groups to share my story, to motivate and inspire, which I delight in doing. It warms my heart to know I am changing the perceptions of young minds through my professional accomplishments.

With confidence, knowledge, and determination, you will perform your duties as a tech girl. When you do your job well, you will show others the true capabilities of women and break down the old stereotypes. Together, we will continue to change society's perceptions of the so-called male-only professions. It might take a while, but we can support each other on this journey.

Summary of Lessons

- A project manager must motivate the teams they lead.
- Accountable teams are those where team members are trusted to make decisions.
- Do not mother your colleagues. Know the limits of your responsibilities.
- Discover what gives you confidence and do it.
- Fill any gaps in your professional knowledge, so you can be the best at what you do.
- Mistakes are for the living; accept that they will happen and learn from them.
- Feedback on your work facilitates growth. Seek it out from those you trust.
- Continued practice sharpens skills.
- Avoid conflict and remind teams of their common goals.
- Families and communities are motivated by strong women. Do your job well and you will inspire others and challenge stereotypes.

CHAPTER 14

Tech Girls In Love

"If You Can't Find a Spouse Who Supports
Your Career, Stay Single."

—Avivah Wittenberg-Cox

Relatives would come to the family home often. Sometimes it was simply to visit; other times to borrow money or request help with accommodation as they tried to find a job in the city. Whatever their reason, I would often hurry my conversations with them and try to get away because they all seemed to disapprove of me wanting to study engineering.

"Don't you want to get married in the future and have children of your own?" they would say with a gasp. "No man will marry an engineer who is always dirty and dressed shabbily. A woman should never be seen untidy and haggard."

I could never comprehend the connection between engineering and being shabby or dirty, so I would mumble something under my breath and hastily exit.

Still, while I didn't agree with my relatives' reasoning, they were sort of right that some men don't want to be in a relationship with a female engineer or, indeed, any ambitious tech girl. But it is important to remember that these men are not worth it! Over the years, my conversations with several female engineers, some married, some divorced, and some still hoping to tie the note with Mr Right, have all boiled down to the fact that professionally ambitious women need partners who support their careers and dreams. Otherwise, they are better off with no partner at all. Anything in between will only lead to unhappiness.

Angela: A Bitter Woman

Angela had been married for ten years and had three beautiful children. Her husband, Ben, was a quality control manager at a local pharmaceutical company. After years of hard work and self-determination, Angela was promoted to chief engineer in her company for her exceptional talent. The other female engineers and I of our community were all challenged by her achievements and proud to have her in our tribe of tech women.

Her company was expanding and setting up another office in Zambia. Angela was the automatic choice to spearhead these operations. The position was not only challenging but came with a good financial package, as well. Her whole family would be well catered for in Zambia. She says she was beaming from ear to ear as she got home to share the great news with her better half.

Her husband would not even let her finish! He told her that it was a non-starter and that they stood to lose out by moving. Where would he get a job in Zambia? Besides, his company was paying him well, and he could afford to support them. Angela argued that her salary and perks would be enough to give them a luxurious life whilst he secured a job. Yet, he would not change his mind and instructed Angela to turn down the offer first thing the following morning. In the blink of an eye, the flame burning inside her was extinguished. The dream of her career jetting off was shot down in an instant. She would stay in her marriage, but as a bitter, unfulfilled woman.

Sadly, many societies put marriage for women above all other ambitions, claiming their duty to their husbands and children must come before anything else.[21] While the man has more freedom to pursue his career goals because he is expected to be ambitious, independent, assertive, and to support the family financially, the woman must focus on being beautiful, compassionate, nurturing, and sympathetic.[22,23] These sorts of stereotypes can prove harmful, especially in relationships where the woman is ambitious, because they will lead the man into stifling his wife's expression and creativity, as well as hindering her personal and professional growth, leaving her unhappy and resentful.

These stereotypes are also harmful to men themselves because it puts so much pressure on them to perform and provide. They feel they need to earn more and occupy more powerful positions than their wives for them to be labelled as "proper men". By eradicating these stereotypes, men can be less sensitive to their wives making more money, which means marriages are happier and families better off. Men will be mentally stronger to pursue their own dreams, even if it means not making as much money, while their wife is the bread-winner of the household. There should never be a reason to doubt your partner or hold them back. A marriage is like a building made of brick and mortar. Both partners need each other to create a strong and stable structure. If one is weak or doesn't support the other, the whole building collapses.

Pamela: "Divorce Was My Only Way Out"

Pamela said she had to divorce her husband, Jim, as she felt he was not supportive of her career and was always pulling her down and holding her back.

"I am about to be named CEO," he would say, repeatedly. "I can't move now." Yet, he had been saying that for six years, using it as an excuse to frustrate Pamela's career. Jim had to be the most selfish guy she had ever come across, she would retort through tight lips.

Well, enough was enough. When an opportunity arose for Pamela to head a company branch in Ghana, she did not hesitate. She was tired of her dreams playing second fiddle in their marriage. Pamela told Jim that she would be leaving for Ghana as she felt the opportunity would be too great to miss. She would be moving with their two young children. He was welcome to join them if he wished to do so.

Three years down the line, Pamela filed for divorce. Jim never made any move to follow them.

And does she have any regrets today? Only that she wishes she had made the decision earlier to spare her career and happiness.

Some men I have interacted with perceive female engineers as being domineering and difficult to "manage". It's utter rubbish. I have colleagues who are married to female engineers and female engineers as friends who are married. Their marriages are as normal as the next one. It takes a confident man, mature in his own right, to take on a confident woman. Anyone who describes a woman as difficult to manage because they have career ambitions is simply insecure in his role as a husband.

It is okay for women to go against societal expectations, especially when it will bring peace and happiness into their lives. However, they must be prepared to face a backlash from society, family, and friends for their perceived rebellious nature. This may be in the form of domestic violence or threats of such violence. You may also be deemed unfit to offer advice on marriage by family and friends or just avoided entirely because they think you are a bad influence.[24] This childish response is not okay, but while it might seem at times like you are alone, there are people and communities who can help. Seek assistance from those you trust in your circle or, if this isn't possible, the support of organisations. Above all, keep a positive mind-set and know that you are worthy of loving and supportive relationships.

Esther: A Jealous Boyfriend

Esther was fresh from graduating when she managed to secure a job at a local engineering company. Unfortunately, she had a possessive boyfriend, Timothy, who did not want her to go on any site visits out of town. Besides claiming site work was not for women, he would say that women should not be exposed to the sun and other harsh weather, else it will ruin their skin.

Occasionally, she would find a way of going on a site visit, anyway, but her phone would ring every ten minutes as Timothy sought to check up on her. In the end, she had to put her phone on silent to avoid any embarrassment and concentrate on her work, only to be accused of being a cheat and not considering his feelings whenever she found the time to call back.

She quickly grew weary of all his whining and feared that he would behave even worse as a husband if he was already acting this way as a boyfriend. Would he ever support her career or would he end up demanding that she stopped working altogether? The signs were all there and Esther decided to walk away from the relationship.

Many cultures encourage male dominance in relationships, with some men even believing it is fine for them to monitor their partner's social media and mobile phones,[25] while women are expected to be submissive. Women are viewed as vessels of beauty foremost; the rest being deemed secondary.

Well, as I have demonstrated, this is a sexist belief that is harmful to everyone involved and it needs to end. Men and women, alike, must speak out against such prejudice.

When women choose their life partner, they should not be encouraged to ignore the writings on the wall. Remember, what you see is what you get. People don't change easily. So, if your partner shows any signs of not supporting your career now, you should not expect that to change after marriage. Instead, choose wisely. Find someone who will support you and help you achieve your dreams.

Like anything else in life, love can be a blessing or a curse. Some tech girls have had successful marriages and others have had to walk away from toxic relationships which lack the proper support and care. But should you stumble in the wake of a bad relationship, put it behind you, dust yourself off, hold your head high, and resume your journey. You only live life once, so make it count. You are responsible for your own life's script and toxic beliefs about marriage and relationships should not hold you back from realising your ambitions or being happy!

CHAPTER 15

Single Parenthood

"Raising a family is difficult enough,
but it's even more difficult for SINGLE
PARENTS struggling to make ends meet.
They don't need more OBSTACLES,
They need more OPPORTUNITIES."

—*Bill Richardson*

feel I am an authority when it comes to speaking about being a single parent. After all, I am one! The journey of becoming pregnant and giving birth to my daughter has had its challenges, but it's been a fulfilling one.

Single motherhood can arise due to a whole variety of circumstances: the death of the husband; divorce; the husband or partner leaving; or a boyfriend who is unwilling to raise a child. Unfortunately, many throughout Africa (and the rest of the world) consider single mothers to be people of loose morals and it is often a case of guilty until proven innocent. So, when I became pregnant while unmarried, I knew I would have to fight this brand going forward.

Sadly, this also meant confronting my own father, who believed that a child should have both of its parents, whether married or not. I had believed this, too, so it had been painful when my partner had told me he did not want to settle down and get married when I got pregnant. Now, I had to rethink my own ideas about the family unit. I felt let down by the person I thought would be with me for the long haul and had to confront the scary notion of raising a child by myself. Motherhood was new to me and I did not know where to start. I did not want to mess up this young life by enacting bad parenting skills. And this was made all the worse because I was the firstborn in my family, and firstborns are tasked with the role of being exemplary to their siblings. I lived with the constant fear that should one of my younger sisters have children of their own without getting married, then I would be considered responsible. (Fortunately, this has not happened so far, so my actions have helped dispel some of these beliefs.)

I also felt guilty for what my mother would have to endure. While I do not like these social stigmas about single mothers, they exist and my mother would be seen by her community as having failed in her motherly duties by allowing her daughter to get pregnant whilst still in her father's house.

So, while knowing I would be a single mother was scary, the experience was made more depressing by the fact that other people would be affected. I believe that our decisions are our own and no one else should be judged for them.

Fortunately, my parents have never let social stigmas get in the way of their love for their children. After speaking with my family and friends for guidance on how I should handle the situation, they gave me the reassurance and confidence to ignore the negative mutterings of the people around me and told me to focus on the bundle of joy that God had blessed me with and which was growing inside of me. At last, I could focus on being the best mother I could be for my daughter.

I named my daughter Tanatswa, which means, "we have been blessed".

My daughter is the ultimate gift and I consider myself fortunate that I now know what it means to put another life above my own.

After Tanatswa was born, I moved to my parent's house, so my mother could guide me on how to look after a newborn baby. She showed me how to bathe, clothe, and feed her. I became more confident as my fragile baby grew bigger and stronger, but my mother continued to help and support me. For example, when my daughter was two years old, I had to move to a new town for work. While I was looking for a new home, I did not want to have to stay in a hotel room with my daughter and the lady I had employed to look after her. I spent a couple of sleepless nights trying to work out how I would go about the whole situation. As ever, my mother put my mind to rest when she told me she could stay with my daughter during the week until I had secured our accommodation.

This arrangement saw me travelling to my parents' home every Friday afternoon and back to work on Monday morning. In my mind, I feared that she would forget my face if I was away from her for too long. Yet, my daughter's toothless grin as I entered the house each Friday reassured me that she remembered me. My heart would melt as I held her close, only to break when I left her again on Monday. But after three months, I got a house and moved in with my daughter.

I was able to be a great single mother to my daughter because I had help. My parents and siblings stood in for me and made sure my daughter was well taken care of in my absence. The knowledge that my child was well looked after gave me peace of mind and enabled me to execute my many responsibilities to the best of my abilities.

Growing up, the only family unit I thought worked was one where there was a father, mother, and their children. But the experience of raising my daughter on my own taught me that single women and men can do just as good a job. I learnt that we need to stop judging other people, especially single mothers, because we cannot know how and why they ended up in their situation, and that any family dynamic can work, so long as the child receives love and support.

If you find yourself in such a situation, do not be distressed. It takes hard work and can be economically and emotionally draining, but you will survive. Seek help where you can and maintain a positive mindset. Your family and friends or the community at large are resources you can tap into for support. And if you have to look further afield for help, there are organisations that can provide single parents with economic and emotional support when they need it.[27,28,29] Investigate the ones in your community to find your best options.

Having a baby is not the end of your career either. Some people can help you by taking care of your child when you go to work. If these networks are not readily available, you can look after your child and return to your career later. You could also find out if there are any support programmes in your locality for mothers wanting to go back to work.

As a single mother, you cannot control what people say about you, but you can control what you say about yourself and what you choose to acknowledge. Cut the negative people from your life and spend time around people who will encourage and support you and bring out your best qualities.

Summary of Lessons

- The family dynamic can take many forms. What's important is that the child receives love and care.
- Single parents can get assistance from family, friends, and organisations.
- A woman can go back to work after birthing and raising her child.

CHAPTER 16

Raising The Daughter I Want

"Make your daughter so capable that you don't have to worry who will marry her! Instead of saving money for her wedding day, spend it well on her education and, most importantly, instead of preparing her for her marriage, prepare her for herself! Teach her self-love & confidence."

—*FamilyLoveGifts Blog*

My daughter is now eighteen. I have tried to raise her in a manner in which the societal webs spun around her would not entangle, restrict, and frustrate her. Instead, her passions have been the driving force behind her choices, while I did my best to offer her guidance and information.

From a young age, I bought my daughter any toy that interested her, irrespective of whether society determined it to be a boy's toy or a girl's toy. She played with remote-controlled cars, dolls, tea party sets, construction vehicles, toy doctor's equipment, puzzles, magnifying glasses, scooters, bicycles, and plastic spanners. And so, she learnt that toys are without gender and developed a wide variety of skills: she could fix her bicycle, plait hair, ride a scooter, and make a cup of tea.

One toy I bought Tanatswa was a Lego set, which she worked on every day after school. She had a special corner in the house for her work, so we would not disturb anything when cleaning. She worked on it for weeks and, when she was done, she called me to see it. Tanatswa had recreated her favourite cartoon characters from TV, complete with all their gadgets and vehicles, including the aeroplanes and cars they used. It was beautiful.

Speaking of Lego, I find their famous 1974 letter to parents around the world echoes my philosophy:

> To Parents,
>
> The urge to create is equally strong in all children. Boys and girls.
>
> It's imagination that counts. Not skill. You build whatever comes into your head, the way you want it. A bed or a truck. A dolls house or a spaceship.
>
> A lot of boys like dolls houses. They're more human than spaceships. A lot of girls prefer spaceships. They're more exciting than dolls houses.
>
> The most important thing is to put the right material in their hands and let them create whatever appeals to them.

In fact, Lego's claims that children are diverse and equally creative are supported by contemporary research. For instance, a UK government report on literacy concluded that 98% of children aged three to five years old demonstrate high levels of creative thinking. Yet, by the time they are aged eight to ten, this figure has plummeted to 32%.[30] Denying girls toys that enhance their creativity means they are less likely to take an interest in careers that require creativity in the future; engineering being one of them. For example, building blocks help children think and problem-solve in three dimensions, which is a useful skill to develop early if one has an interest in technical careers. If we don't give building blocks to girls, we give boys an unfair advantage by allowing them to develop this skill earlier on. Let's not disqualify our girls before the race even begins.

So, I invite parents to follow Lego's advice to ensure that our girls and boys are not deprived of their natural gifts and callings because we limited their creative experiences.

And to the young people reading this book, free yourselves from limiting beliefs that serve no purpose other than to restrict your ability to become the best version of yourselves.

With this foundation, Tanatswa grew up building and fixing things. Her inquisitive mind was always on the lookout to find the solution to one problem or another.

One weekend, I saw her picking up bits and pieces from around the house: wire, board, a battery, and a bulb. By the end of the day, she had built a side lamp for her room. She salvaged an old bicycle with no chains and tyres and fixed it up to make it rideable again. I helped her get the missing parts she needed from town, but she tensioned the chains, adjusted the brakes, and fit the new tyres by herself. I was amazed at how someone so young could do such things. And when I bought her a skateboard, she assessed that the wheels were too stiff and borrowed my screwdrivers to loosen them and reduce the friction.

Of course, some of her efforts were more successful than others (and some escapades were near misses in which she avoided disaster by a whisker). One such event occurred when I discussed with her how our neighbourhood was preyed upon by robbers. I wanted to get myself a pepper spray, but when we searched for somewhere to buy them in the newspaper, they were a bit pricey and I decided I would have to wait to get one.

The following day, Tanatswa decided she'd make some pepper spray, instead. She put some methylated spirit into a bowl and attempted to thicken it by applying heat. Unfortunately, she had chosen the carpet as her workstation. So, when she lit a match to carry out her chemical process, a flame sprang up, the methylated spirit spilt over, and the carpet caught fire. Luckily, the fire did not spread and just left behind a black circular patch. When I got home from work, I asked about the patch, and she told me she had accidentally placed a hot pot on the carpet. It was only years later that she admitted what had really transpired. That had been a narrow escape for sure, although I admire her endeavour. After all, we tech girls must be prepared to experiment and try new things if we want to innovate and change the world.

But what toys and activities we allow our children to enjoy in the home are not the only way we influence how they perceive themselves in society, knowingly or otherwise. There are plenty of other biases that we pass on to our children because we think something should be done a certain way, not realising the harm we are doing to how our sons and daughters perceive the world and themselves.

I plaited Tanatswa's hair myself from when she was a baby. I would tie ribbons and all the lovely, fancy things mothers love to put in their babies' hair. She had gorgeous, thick Afro hair that covered her tiny head.

But when she was nine years old, Tanatswa rushed into my room and said, "Mum, can you please take me to the hairdresser to have my hair cut. I want a length that is easier to brush."

"Why would you want to cut off all that beautiful hair?" I gasped.

"It's always painful having my hair plaited. These women shove my head this way and that and pull my hair until my head aches and it hurts for a long time after they finish."

I could relate to that. I remembered the times I had sat up in bed after a hairdo because putting my head on the pillow was too painful. There had been times when I couldn't even smile because it hurt so much. Was that something I wished for someone so young? Surely, the motto "no pain no gain" does not apply to a child.

"OK, dear," I said. "We will go to the hairdresser at the weekend."

"Thanks, Mum!" she said, with a great sigh of relief and ran off to play.

But it's not that easy, is it? One of the reasons we continue to perpetuate traditions, even when they are undesirable, is because other people put pressure on us. I remember going hoarse as I parroted the same answer to every woman at the hairdresser. Yes, my daughter did not want the hair anymore, so it had to go. And yes, I had allowed it! Some women mentioned that a girl had to look pretty all the time and her hair was her crown. At that age, who cares about pretty? Subconsciously, those women were of the mind that girls should already be preparing for a suitor for marriage. The girl was nine! Adding to this, another "wise" women said that cutting Tanatswa's hair would make it difficult for people to distinguish whether she was a boy or girl. Distinction for what purpose? We knew her sex at home, as did her teachers and classmates in school.

Gender stereotypes and patriarchal values undermine and place severe limitations on girls concerning their right to be heard and their right to make decisions about their own bodies. Girls should be permitted and encouraged to share their views.[31]

Dictating what girls can and cannot do starts way in their infancy. Is it surprising, then, that decisions to do with their careers are so skewed or even made for them? Girls are taught by many societies to shut up and look pretty. Should we really be shocked that, after a childhood of being told what to do by the men or older women in their lives, many women expect to be told what careers to embark on, which jobs will suit them, and which ones will be too difficult for them?

Now, consider the wasted potential if, as the research shows, and I have proven with my own career, women are just as capable, if given the same support and opportunities as men.

Do not stifle your daughter's voice in the home. Allow her to make decisions about her body, her hair, her clothes, and her interests. When she feels she can make decisions about herself, she will understand herself better. She will become more confident with who she is, her self-esteem will grow, and she will understand what makes her happy. Over time, she will use this confidence in other spheres of her life, such as deciding on the career path that is right for her.

Of course, your parental guidance will be required. There will be times your daughter tries to take things too far. But all children do this, yet we do not tell boys they are incapable of making their own choices. We do not tell boys they are less than girls. Let's value our children's confidence and self-worth as much as we value their social etiquette, and we will all enjoy a happier and more fulfilled society.

From an early age, we have told our girls that looking pretty is a priority above everything else. That all she had to do was look pretty and beautiful and her life was set. But life has more to offer than just beauty. A girl has more to achieve than just prettiness. No wonder our girls are obsessed with their looks. They do not worry about poor grades, as long as they are the prettiest girl in school. As a result, they are less competitive in school or sports. Meanwhile, boys are pushed to be high achievers, so that is what they become.

My daughter is proof there is another way. She is very sporty and I have supported her in every way possible. I have driven her at four in the morning to catch the school bus to travel to hockey tournaments. I would dash from the office to her cross-country races to cheer her on. I have come to swimming galas just in time to give her a thumbs-up before the whistle is blown for the race to start. She has sought me out at athletics events and found me grinning and jumping up and down among the crowd, excitedly screaming her name. I have sprinted out from work during my lunchtime to buy her a pair of shorts because she wanted to play cricket the following day, or to buy her soccer boots before the weekend game. And I have stayed up all night to sew her a tutu for gymnastics because I could not afford the ones on sale.

On and on it went. She had fun and exposed herself to new experiences, all the while building her confidence and learning what she enjoyed.

Of course, as parents, we sometimes have commitments we cannot escape. On the occasions I could not turn up to support my daughter, I would explain to her why. If possible, I would ask either my sister or brother to stand in for me. Naturally, my daughter would be disappointed if I couldn't come to an event, but she always understood that I was juggling many balls in the air to provide us both with the life we enjoyed.

Ultimately, I wanted Tanatswa to appreciate that sport, like any interest, is not about gender but capability and passion. I wanted her to know what boys can do, girls can do, too, and she proved it! She was the only girl at school playing cricket, despite the snide comments of the other mothers. She was the best soccer player in her school. And she did all this while participating in other sports, like cross-country running and swimming.

I have raised my daughter to confront norms that expect girls to stick to the traditional sports labelled as appropriate for them. I have knocked on many headmasters' doors because they had no soccer team for girls. Why not? Because the girls don't want to play, I am told. No! It is because the teachers have not encouraged them to play. Their silence has communicated to the girls that they cannot play soccer because it's a boy's game. They are feeding the monstrous belief that only boys can or should kick a soccer ball.

Much of this bias goes back to how we, as a society, expect girls to look and behave. Some believe that certain sports, like soccer and rugby, are unladylike because they are rough. Instead, they say, girls must be refined, a girl must not shout. Who would want to marry a girl that behaves otherwise? And so, everything dovetails back to marriage for girls. At ten years of age, often younger, we are preparing our girls for marriage. Is this what we want for them after having sent them to school for many years? Why do it if we don't truly value their education? I say, let girls be girls, let boys be boys, but, above all, let children be children. We need to break these barriers in sports, which will give us headway to break barriers in other spheres of our daughters' lives. After all, victory in one sphere always propagates into victory in other spheres, as well.

What type of daughter are you raising? Are you raising a girl who will grow into a woman to blaze her trail in this world, making an impact and leaving her mark? A fearless woman, who knows what she wants and is brave enough to go after it? You can raise such a daughter, but it takes effort. Consider what you tell her, for example, when she discusses her passions and interests with you. Are you discouraging her from doing certain things because they are not "girly"? What does she hear you say about her in the community? What does she hear you say about other people's daughters when you have your friends over for a cup of tea? Always remember, as parents, you play a huge role in supporting, nurturing, and cherishing your children's ideas. Your words and behaviour will shape how those ideas blossom into the beliefs that dominate the rest of their lives. I challenge you, parents, to smash down the barriers and interrogate those stereotypes holding our girls back. We owe it to them.

There is one more lesson I have tried to teach my daughter and that is to know that she should not take herself too seriously. Life will throw curveballs at her, but in every dark cloud, there is always a silver lining. Like my father taught me, she should know it is alright to cry, but also, one needs to know when it is time to wipe away their tears and carry on.

This includes feeling doubt. Doubt about our interests and goals in life.

Being a mum who is an engineer, many people to whom I have introduced my daughter have asked me whether she will be an engineer, as well. I always looked to Tanatswa to answer for herself, who would smile politely and slowly shake her head. I have never put any pressure on her to follow in my footsteps because I believe our children need to follow their own passions and make their own choices. We should not live our dreams through them. As a young woman, Tanatswa is still exploring her options. She may be interested in sports science today, criminology tomorrow, and something I have never heard of the day after that. But this is nothing for parents to worry about; it is quite normal at such an age. Eventually, she will settle on something she likes. And when she does, I will be here to support her decision.

Some of you reading this may be worried that a young person who does not decide their career early will spend their lives catching up or will continue to change their minds forever. Well, a friend's daughter recently graduated in chemical engineering. I met them one day and asked the daughter about her plans. She told me she was back in university studying accounting because she had never wanted to study chemical engineering in the first place. Her parents had made her study the degree, but she didn't find it stimulating. I turned and looked at my friend, who could only manage a feeble grin. The girl had wasted four years only to go back to university, again.

Parents, do not be tempted to choose careers for your children based on what you regard as classy or prestigious. Allow your children to iden-tify their own interests, and then gently guide their strengths, so they can nurture their skills and grow them into what may become their career. If they choose a career they enjoy and which stimulates them, they will be more likely to stay in it for longer and to thrive.

Summary of Lessons

- The creativity of children is limited when others filter the experiences and tools they can enjoy.
- There is far more to life than being pretty.
- Girls must be allowed to voice what they want for them-selves, their bodies, and their career.
- Girls should be encouraged to participate in all sports.
- Parents must not select careers for their children.
- Parents should allow their children to discover their in-terests and, then, identify and nurture their strengths.

EPILOGUE

"Success isn't about how much money you make,
it's about the difference you make in people's lives."
—Michelle Obama

I have endeavoured to cover as much of my tech journey in this book in the hopes of inspiring you with examples of my successes and challenges and the lessons I have learnt along the way. I have done this by recalling personal conversations with my mother and father, which shaped me into the woman I am today, and events that occurred in both my childhood and adulthood. My mother's story, in particular, reinforces the fact that women are powerful in their own right and have what it takes to overcome the many obstacles they face in patriarchal societies. This has been the core of what my book has tried to portray.

My network of female engineers and women who are passionate about STEM careers has been a great source of inspiration to me as I wrote this book. The challenges, pains, and joys they have experienced in the pursuit of their dreams gave me the idea of putting my experiences to paper, so that they could be inspired, challenged, and motivated to realise that their experiences were not peculiar to them alone, but common to most women with similar ambitions. Likewise, I wanted to reinforce that these challenges are not insurmountable, but that, with perseverance, a positive mindset, and a support network, they can be overcome. Therefore, I will consider it a reward if anyone should read this book and identify themselves, or someone they know, with any of my anecdotes and lessons.

Having been born into an educated, middle-class family, I enjoyed a very happy childhood. I was privileged to play at the amusement park or visit places where I could see animals. I loved to visit my grandmother and eat dried meat and the chicken she always prepared so well. Christmas time was a time when the extended family, which included my cousins, and my own would gather at my grandmother's home to celebrate with party hats and balloons for all the children.

As I grew older and left for primary and then secondary school, I had the support of my parents. They encouraged me to work hard and attain good grades. This foundation saw me through university to graduate with Honours in Civil Engineering. Not content, I sought to better myself and be more competitive, so I worked to attain a Master's degree in Water Resources Engineering and, later, in 2013, a Master's in Business Administration.

I have worked in various roles in the public sector, non-governmental organisations, and the private sector, I have had the opportunity to lead project teams in Zimbabwe, Uganda, and Tanzania, and I continue to thrive off the positive impact I contribute to communities through the construction of improved water and sanitation infrastructure.

During my mid-career, I had my daughter, who I have raised as a single parent to adulthood. Through the foundations of resilience and strength instilled in me from a young age, and the support of my family, I was able to overcome this life-changing hurdle to raise a strong and talented woman who has given me so much joy. I am happy and content to leave a legacy in the form of my work and my daughter, who herself shows such great promise.

As an engineer, I have faced the stigma of being labelled a secretary because an engineer was a "man's job". I have been exposed to sexual harassment in the workplace, with one incident leaving me unemployed and without any income, despite having a baby to feed. I have been ignored on project sites and meetings because a woman's voice did not matter. Men I worked with would not allow themselves to rise above the patriarchy that had shaped their lives when they were growing up, and so they risked passing this toxic attitude onto their children. I have been accused of being too emotional and been punished for it by not having my work contracts renewed or being passed up for promotion. And I have learnt to fight against the discrimination and oppression of women in engineering with diplomacy, a cool head, and a sharp tongue.

My tech journey does not end with this book. As I move forward, it is my hope and desire:

- To continue to bring awareness to parents, so they can encourage their daughters to study STEM subjects and pursue STEM careers.
- To continue to inspire junior engineers to overcome the hurdles in their workplace.
- To inspire young girls dreaming about how they can improve their communities and the world at large, and to view STEM careers as a legitimate pathway.
- To educate the girls on engineering and how it can impact our communities.
- To prove to girls that, with the right motivation and determination, they are unstoppable.
- That parents who read this book will challenge themselves and their ideas to raise their daughters in a manner that inspires an interest in STEM.
- For girls and their communities to fight for their right to be independent enough to choose their own academic and career paths.
- That the boys and men who read this book challenge any beliefs they may have about STEM careers being only for boys or that girls are inferior or incapable.

Girl, stand up proud,
Speak out loud,
Refuse to be silenced,
Come forth, from beneath the shadows,
Believe in yourself,
Intelligent you are,
Beautiful you are,
Strong you are,
Stand up proud,
Speak out loud,
Because, yes,
You can and you will!
Girl, you are worthy

REFERENCES

1   Everyculture.com, 2020. Culture of Zimbabwe - History, People, Traditions, Women, Beliefs, Food, Customs, Family, Social. [online] Available at: https://www.everyculture.com/To-Z/Zimbabwe.html [Accessed December 2020].

2   Tradingeconomics.com, 2020. Zimbabwe - Proportion Of Seats Held By Women In National Parliaments - 1990-2020 Data. [online] Available at: https://tradingeconomics.com/zimbabwe/proportion-of-seats-held-by-women-in-national-parliaments-percent-wb-data.html [Accessed 4 December 2020].

3   Cultural Atlas. 2020. Zimbabwean Culture - Religion. [online] Available at: https://culturalatlas.sbs.com.au/zimbabwean-culture/zimbabwean-culture-religion [Accessed November 2020].

4   Nunner-Winkler, G., 2001. Sex-role Development and Education. In: N. Smelser and P. Baltes, ed., *International Encyclopedia of the Social & Behavioral Sciences, 1ˢᵗ ed*. Pergamon, pp.13958-13961.

5   De La Rosa, S., 2020. Survey: Female Students Still Lack Confidence In Math, Science. [online] *K-12 Dive*. Available at: https://www.educationdive.com/news/survey-female-students-still-lack-confidence-in-math-science/575678/ [Accessed December 2020].

6   Lynkova, D., 2020. 27+ Women In Technology Statistics: What's New In 2020? [online] *TechJury*. Available at: https://techjury.net/blog/women-in-technology-statistics/ [Accessed December 2020].

7   Kapner, L., 2017. The Myth Of The Math Brain. [online] *Giftededucationcommunicator.com*. Available at: http://

giftededucationcommunicator.com/gec-spring-2017/the-myth-of-the-math-brain/ [Accessed November 2020].

8   AAUW, n.d. The Myth Of The Male Math Brain. [online] Available at: https://www.aauw.org/resources/article/the-myth-of-the-male-math-brain/ [Accessed November 2020].

9   Marcus, R. and Page, E., 2014. *Drivers Of Change In Gender Norms.* [online] London, UK: Overseas Development Institute, p.12. Available at: https://www.odi.org/sites/odi.org.uk/files/odi-assets/publications-opinion-files/9184.pdf [Accessed December 2020].

10   Tull, M., 2019. Why Masculine Gender Norms Make PTSD Worse. [online] *verywell mind.* Available at: https://www.verywellmind.com/the-consequences-of-male-gender-role-stress-2797513 [Accessed December 2020].

11   Sound Vision, n.d. Clash Between Parents & Children On Career Choices. [online] Available at: https://www.soundvision.com/article/clash-between-parents-children-on-career-choices [Accessed December 2020].

12   AAUW, n.d. The Myth Of The Male Math Brain.

13   Milgrom-Elcott, T., 2019. When It Comes To Women In STEM Roles, The Results Are Golden. [online] *Forbes.* Available at: https://www.forbes.com/sites/taliamilgromelcott/2019/01/03/when-it-comes-to-women-in-stem-roles-the-results-are-golden/?sh=59d20a61e322 [Accessed November 2020].

14   Forum for African Women Educationalists: FAWE, n.d. About FAWE. [online] Available at: http://fawe.org/about-fawe/ [Accessed December 2020].

15   Huyer, S., 2018. Is The Gender Gap Narrowing In Science And Engineering? UNESCO Science Report. [online] *UNESCO,* p.92. Available at: https://en.unesco.org/sites/default/files/usr15_is_the_gender_gap_narrowing_in_science_and_engineering.pdf [Accessed November 2020].

16   Lynkova, D., 2020. 27+ Women In Technology Statistics: What's New In 2020?

17   World Economic Forum, 2016. The Global Gender Gap Report. [online] Available at: http://www3.weforum.org/docs/GGGR16/WEF_Global_Gender_Gap_Report_2016.pdf [Accessed December 2020].

18 Zhakata, W., 2018. Survey Gives Shocking Sexual Abuse Statistics. [online] *The Herald.* Available at: https://www.herald.co.zw/survey-gives-shocking-sexual-abuse-statistics/ [Accessed November 2020].

19 Mapuranga, B., Musodza, B. and Tom, T., 2015. Sexual Harassment of Female Employees at a State University in Zimbabwe. *Developing Country Studies,* 5(12), p.28.

20 Mapuranga, B., Musodza, B. and Tom, T., 2015, Sexual Harassment of Female Employees at a State University in Zimbabwe, p.28.

21 Oxfam International, n.d. Ten Harmful Beliefs That Perpetuate Violence Against Women And Girls. [online] Available at: https://www.oxfam.org/en/ten-harmful-beliefs-perpetuate-violence-against-women-and-girls [Accessed December 2020].

22 United Nations, 2011. Men In Families And Family Policy In A Changing World. [online] New York: Department of Economic and Social Affairs. Available at: https://www.un.org/esa/socdev/family/docs/men-in-families.pdf [Accessed November 2020].

23 OHCHR, 2013. Gender Stereotyping As A Human Rights Violation.

24 Marcus, R. and Page, E., 2014. Drivers Of Change In Gender Norms.

25 Oxfam International, n.d. Ten Harmful Beliefs That Perpetuate Violence Against Women And Girls.

26 Watson, C. and Harper, C., 2013. *Adolescent Girls And Gender Justice: Understanding Key Capability Domains Across A Variety Of Socio-Cultural Settings.* London, UK: Overseas Development Institute.

27 Camfed, n.d. Zimbabwe, Camfed And Mother Support Groups. [PDF] Available at: https://www.globalgiving.org/pfil/2046/projdoc.pdf [Accessed November 2020].

28 Facebook.com, n.d. Single Mothers Foundation. [online] Available at: https://www.facebook.com/Single-Mothers-Foundation-180446802523255/about/?ref=page_internal [Accessed December 2020].

29 Meetup, n.d. Single Moms Support Groups. [online] Available at: https://www.meetup.com/topics/single-moms-support/ [Accessed December 2020].

30 Anthony, M., n.d. Creative Development In Adolescents. [online] *Scholastic.* Available at: https://www.scholastic.com/parents/family-life/creativity-and-critical-thinking/development-milestones/creative-development-adolescents.html [Accessed December 2020].

31 UN Committee on the Rights of the Child (CRC), General comment No. 12 (2009): The right of the child to be heard, 20 July 2009, CRC/C/GC/12.

APPENDIX

Takeaways

GIRLS & YOUNG ENGINEERS

- It is possible to be a woman and have a fulfilling career in STEM. After all, another girl did it!
- Believe in yourself that you can accomplish your dreams. The rest will align with this belief along the way.
- It is alright to fail and make mistakes. It is common among us all. Learn from your failures and emerge stronger, ready to try again.
- Female leaders and bosses can and do cry. Just don't do it in public or else you will risk losing the respect of your colleagues.
- Be knowledgeable about what you do. That is the only way you will prove yourself and earn the respect of your colleagues.
- Practice makes perfect. Keep working on your skills to improve your knowledge, your abilities, and yourself.
- Silence has never solved anything. Speak up for the changes you want to see happen.
- Don't worry about what other people think. It is not their story you are living but your own. Go, girl. Continue writing and acting out your script.

- You can never please everyone. Even when you lie flat on the floor for people to walk all over you, they will still say you are not lying flat enough.
- You must be emotionally intelligent in your social and professional lives. Learn to understand, use, and manage your emotions in positive ways to relieve stress, communicate effectively, empathise with others, overcome challenges, and defuse conflict.
- Choose your battles wisely. We only have so much energy, so don't feel you have to fight every day.
- It is okay to blow your own horn once in a while.
- Had a bad day? Don't worry. Tomorrow is a new day to start again with a clean slate.
- Do not feel guilty about wanting to nurture yourself first. Being in a good place physically, mentally, and emotionally will mean you are stronger to nurture those around you.
- Even when the odds seem like they are against you, don't give in. You are stronger than you think.

PARENTS

- From infancy, buy your children a range of age-appropriate clothes, toys, and books, irrespective of gender, to encourage their creativity and interests from an early age.
- Champion your daughters' dreams, including if they show an interest in STEM subjects/careers.
- Always be there to support your daughters and sons in their passions.
- Assign chores to your children equally and have them rotate their responsibilities.
- Allow your daughters to make their own choices about their bodies and their interests.

- Speak positively about your daughters and other girls and women, in general, to encourage them to develop a positive mindset about themselves and other women.
- Negative affirmations have the power to destroy our children. Do not tell them they are stupid or useless every time you think they have messed up.
- Show your children you are proud of them and that they have what it takes to succeed.
- You have a pivotal role to play in shaping your children as they believe and accept what you say more than when they hear it from someone else.
- Not everything can be bought with money. Make time to be with, speak with, and support your children. A word of encouragement from you boosts your child's confidence and desire to succeed.

MEN & WOMEN

- Do not shield sexual harassment perpetrators in the workplace, but work to expose them.
- Strive for laws and regulations that are gender-sensitive by including women in the decision-making process, as well.
- Do not perpetuate gender stereotypes. Practise equal rights and roles in your life and at home, and speak out for the changes you want to see in your communities.
- As women, let us fix each other's crowns by being there to encourage and support one another.
- Let us acknowledge women in STEM and other male-dominated careers as being equals to their male counterparts.

MEN & BOYS

- It is okay to relax and let someone else be in charge or for your partner to make more money than you. It does not make you any less of a man.
- A good man is one who supports his partner and children in the pursuit of their ambitions.
- Do not despise or look down on women. Women can do what men can do and everyone can learn from each other and achieve more by working together.

Printed in Great Britain
by Amazon

40481464R00084